Praise for B

"Upon implementing Brain-centric Design at Nike, our training time and attrition were reduced substantially, and our learners (athletes) not only understood their positions better, but also reached their goals faster and were scored higher by our consumers on customer satisfaction surveys."

— Michele Jordan, Fortune 100 Learning Director

"I've engaged Brain-centric Design at two Fortune 100s, with identical results: better employees in about 40% less time. Delivering training the way the brain accepts new information and how people love to learn yields a happier, adaptive, and stronger employee from new hires through management. There are critical components to world-class service delivery, and a key foundational pillar is exceptional talent with exceptional learning and development practices. It has been my experience that Brain-centric Design is a key to equipping and preparing human capital to achieve an enterprise's goals."

— Jason Clement, service executive with 25+ years of experience at leading Fortune 100 companies

"I was never a fan of the *(Whatever) for Dummies* books, but if ever a subject needed to be simplified, it would be neuroscience. Carr & O'Mahony have effectively done that for us, making it clear how the brain processes new information and why humans love to learn."

— Roy H. Williams, author of the *New York Times* and *Wall Street Journal* best-selling Wizard of Ads trilogy of business books

"You arrived at this page in a quest for answers, and Brain-centric Design will provide them, if you allow. Having witnessed the creation of this process from the beginning, [I know that] Brain-centric Design is not just another clever package. It is a process that invites each of us to lean in and become interactive in learning, enabling us to grasp topics easily, quickly, and most importantly, with vastly greater retention. Brain-centric Design with Rich Carr and Dr. Kieran O'Mahony will activate and enhance your ability to learn in a growth mindset that will forever change the way you learn, think, and do. In today's fast-paced, high-tech world, it is gratifying to learn that the human brain is viable, necessary, and easy to manage."

— Ken Robinson, Department of Defense

"There must be a way for hardheads like myself to learn how to learn that does not include years of solitary confinement. If you're reading this, then you've likely found it. If Brain-centric Design had been a resource for my younger self, perhaps this testimonial would have been written by Master Chief Brazee, US Navy rather than Inmate #797180."

— Alan Brazee, Washington State Prison Inmate #797180

"Brain-centric Design took the guesswork out of the classroom and highlighted the scientific reasons behind the success. It felt great to identify the positive traits of cognitive flexibility, social—emotional engagement, and adaptive expertise that I already possessed."

— Ellen Thompson, Fortune 100 Learning & Quality Specialist

Brain-centric Design

The Surprising Neuroscience
Behind Learning With
Deep Understanding

By
Rich Carr, BcID
Dr. Kieran O'Mahony, FRGS

Hardback ISBN: 978-1-944602-22-2
Paperback ISBN: 978-1-944602-50-5
Audiobook ISBN: 978-1-944602-51-2

Thanet House Publishing
848 N. Rainbow Blvd. #750
Las Vegas, NV 89107

Cover Design by Geoffrey Neill
Editing by Julia T. Willson
Interior Layout by Soumi Goswami and Laura Howard
Illustrations by Gabriele Bonavera

Publisher's Cataloging-In-Publication Data
(Prepared by The Donohue Group, Inc.)

Names: Carr, Rich, 1963- author. | O'Mahony, Kieran, 1953- author. |
    Bonavera, Gabriele, illustrator.
Title: Brain-centric Design : the surprising neuroscience behind learning
    with deep understanding / by Rich Carr, CRME, Dr. Kieran O'Mahony,
    FRGS ; [illustrations by Gabriele Bonavera].
Description: Las Vegas, NV : Thanet House Publishing, [2019] | Includes
    bibliographical references and index.
Identifiers: ISBN 9781944602222 (hardcover) | ISBN 9781944602505
    (paperback) | ISBN 9781944602529 (ebook)
Subjects: LCSH: Learning--Physiological aspects. | Comprehension--
    Physiological aspects. | Brain--Psychophysiology. | Neurosciences. |
    Learning, Psychology of.
Classification: LCC QP408 .C37 2019 (print) | LCC QP408 (ebook) | DDC
    612.8/233--dc23

Brain-centric Design is available for bulk orders! Contact info@thanethousebooks.com for more information.

To educators everywhere, no matter
your classroom: trainers, instructional designers,
facilitators, sellers, teachers, managers, and parents.
We all have brains. Seize your unlimited potential!

Contents

Foreword

Let's face it. We have each spent hours, weeks, even years of our lives sitting in boring classrooms, captive to the whims of teachers, the drudgery of coursework, and the banality of content. How many classes have I painfully endured staring at a bright white projection screen, struggling to pay attention as the teacher's monotonous voice reads aloud hundreds of text-heavy slides? Just thinking about it makes my head ache, not to mention my eyes, backside, and brain.

The best (or worst) example occurred a few years ago. I was looking forward to a week-long Trainer Certification Summit with my peers and training teams from around the globe. Guest speakers and presentations packed the schedule. Despite my enthusiasm, by lunchtime on Day 2, I struggled to keep my mind from wandering. By Day 3, the course had fallen behind schedule and I fantasized ways to escape. By Day 4, I was noticeably and uncharacteristically despondent. My brain felt like it had shut down.

As I remember it now, what endures is the feeling that this was indisputably the longest week of my professional life…and man, those chairs were uncomfortable. What I recall about the material is the sheer volume and total inaccessibility of it. Sure, I left with a binder filled with copies of the text, graphs, and charts from the slides that I had been staring at all week. However, I was still perplexed by the method, fried by the experience, and clueless on how to use any of it.

Why couldn't I pay better attention? I had willingly gone there, ready to learn new stuff. I needed this information for my job. I was interested in the material. I decided that I'm just not suited to long learning events with tons of material, and that I would have to suck it up and figure out how to make it work. Somehow, I still knew it was going to be okay. I was okay. I resolved that training can be hard, especially when it's tedious and boring.

Tedious and boring are not two words I would choose to describe who I am or what I do. As a Learning and Development Lead for the largest seller of athletic footwear and apparel in the world, I am responsible for the education, development, coaching, and continuous improvement of 30 trainers and 1,000 digital commerce employees in call centers on multiple continents. I cannot afford to be either tedious or boring when designing and delivering learning that directly impacts our people, programs, and consumer experience.

What bothered me most about the conference is that our brand innovations inspire and motivate millions, yet our training was stagnant. It's not that we didn't try new things. We went web-based, we blended, we flipped. Despite our efforts, the results were the same old problems.

Trainers were exhausted and trainees were bored. Dropouts were at a premium, so Human Resources continuously found new hires to fill training classes. Trainees emerged unsure, uninformed, and underperforming into an environment that demanded confident, capable, and consistent performers. Employee engagement was low and attrition was high. The company was accelerating and the consumer was evolving, but our consumer experience and our sales were declining.

To put it mildly, I was looking for solutions. We needed better training and we needed it fast. It had to be good, it had to be efficient, and it had to be effective. And, of course, it had to be within budget. I knew there wasn't going to be a cure-all, but there had to be something better than what we had.

At the time, Brain-centric Design was entirely off my radar. I wasn't even thinking about neuroscience in terms of training in the workplace.

In hindsight, I was no different from other training teams at my company, in our industry, or any modern industry, for that matter. Though it seems absurd to me now, there is a blind spot for the vital role the brain plays in teaching and learning. Today, I see this oversight as a catastrophic liability for all of us in the fields of instructional design, teaching, coaching, training, and talent development. We all want a happy, thriving, self-reliant, and dedicated workforce that reflects the values of our company. However, we are stuck training in an archaic way where teaching is stressful, learning is difficult, and outcomes are insufficient.

It's logical to say, "How can you use the word *archaic*? We use the most advanced systems with collaborative technologies in state-of-the-art classrooms!" We may use the latest technologies, but we also use a reward and punishment archetype for designing, delivering, and managing knowledge in an age where we are inundated with information and starved for insight.

But then, Rich and Kieran entered the room with the solution that changed everything.

Their workshop "The Neuroscience of Learning" was the main event, and I was front and center. It was the most engaging, informative, fun, and impactful learning experience I had attended in a very long time. I was elated and optimistic, and couldn't wait to learn more. Luckily, I didn't have to wait long.

Rich and Kieran were facilitating our upcoming week-long Trainer Certification Summit. Hope and excitement replaced any dread or anxiety left over from my previous summit experience. Even now, I can recall (in vivid detail) the videos we watched, the posters we drew, the topics we discussed, and the games we played. Each day had a similar structure with a variety of activities, and we kept on schedule. It was fast-paced, yet easy to follow. There was music, laughter, and an abundance of aha moments. I was at home in this creative, collaborative, and nonthreatening learning environment. Learning felt effortless. At the end of the summit, I left with a notebook filled with thoughts and ideas. I knew how to apply what I had learned, and I knew I could never go back to doing things the way I had done them before.

As a learner, Brain-centric Design (BcD) exceeded my expectations. When learning is effortless, it's a big deal. As a teacher, my north star became "Make learning feel effortless."

I embraced BcD from the get-go. It just felt right. In retrospect, the BcD approach to learning was compatible with our company's approach to business. It's an incredibly complex organization that delivers at an altitude and velocity that others won't even attempt. BcD makes perfect sense for a company that has never settled for the status quo.

But it wasn't just that. When I say BcD felt right, I mean that I was already doing a lot of the same things out of intuition and lucky guesses. In my approach to training, I did what I thought felt right and got results…at least some of the time. Now I have a scientific explanation of why doing something one way always worked, and why doing something any other way never could.

BcD took the guesswork out of the classroom and highlighted the scientific reasons behind the success. It felt great to identify the positive traits of cognitive flexibility, social-emotional engagement, and adaptive expertise that I already possessed. At the same time, I had to be honest with myself and recognize that my approach to teaching was unintentionally creating barriers and making learning difficult. I was ready to eliminate the things that would never work and double down on the things that always would. To do that, I would also have to embrace vulnerability.

The next time I stood at the front of the classroom, I was looking at it in a new light. I was no longer a trainer with an audience; I was a BcD facilitator with a room full of collaborators. Each day was carefully structured and planned around a central idea. The central idea was explored through a variety of methods, including independent research, e-learning modules, videos, process maps, storytelling, and interactive exercises, which always led to individual reflection followed by group discussion. I loved that everyone had a way to participate and make sense of new information. They asked questions and received answers that were meaningful to them. They were engaging with the content, cooperating, generating ideas, arriving at conclusions, willing to make mistakes, and having fun. **I was witness to a transformation, right there in my training room: students took control of their learning.**

This approach to facilitation felt like hosting a well-planned party for guests I had never met before. Partygoers need to feel welcome, comfortable, and included. Like any gracious host, BcD enabled me to initiate conversations that spontaneously took place while encouraging everyone to interact with each other. Several carefully scripted activities were planned throughout the course of this party that were fun, engaging, and meaningfully brain-centric. The party was lively, social, and a total success. It was exhausting, but the right kind of exhausting, where I knew it was worth the effort and I was excited to do it again.

In the past, our training had involved traditional tactics like...

- Watch this video.
- Pay attention to these slides.
- Read this handout.
- Take this quiz.

We found that students struggled with content that was conceptually difficult, they didn't react well to topics that were less appealing, and they were terrified to make a mistake. However, with the neuroscientific approach to training, not only were new hires able to tackle complicated subject matter with ease, they could articulate why the information was necessary, when to apply it on the job, and how to connect it to the consumer experience.

For me, the most satisfying result of BcD was witnessing my students recognize the opportunity to contribute to the team fully and genuinely enjoy their work. For my bosses, their satisfaction came from reduced training costs, decreased attrition, higher consumer satisfaction scores, and increased sales.

BcD is the closest thing to a cure-all that I've ever seen.

From then on, I have been all about BcD. I have no doubt you will be too. In truth, understanding the brain's role in learning influenced all aspects of my life. And many things in my daily routine have improved as a result. My self-care, parenting, personal and professional relationships, and job performance all benefit from a refined understanding of how my brain works.

I am privileged to have been a part of the evolution of this marvelous way of teaching and learning in our workplaces. I am so excited for you to read this fabulous book!

Ellen Thompson
BcD Geek, Facilitation Fanatic, Neuroscience Nerd

The Beginning Of BcD

Brain-centric Design is as much a story of chance as it is a circuitous journey across continents and time. That Rich and Kieran would meet was highly improbable. Rich is all-American; Kieran is all-Irish. Their backgrounds are so different that according to any normal course of events, they would never have had the opportunity to collaborate even in the most mundane of circumstances. But in the case of Brain-centric Design (BcD), they are changing the way corporate America conducts itself in areas like talent development, training, retention, and implicit bias. They are also significantly influencing the way that teachers, salespeople, and parents present information to their respective audiences.

The application of BcD is as limitless as the creativity of whomever uses it.

*　　*　　*

The year 1981 was tumultuous for both Rich and Kieran. It was a year of questioning and change. Yet it was the year that laid the foundation for the fortuitous meeting that brought this book to life.

Rich's Story

The year before my high school graduation in 1981, The Police released their third studio album, *Zenyatta Mondatta*. The album features two hit singles, one of which I listened to over and over on my cassette player (volume on high), in my dad's '72 Chevy

pickup, fully equipped with a CB radio and the gun rack I had made in woodshop. That's when I heard that lyric:

Poets, priests, and politicians,
Have words to thank for their positions.

Remember, that record came out in the era of Reagan and Gorbachev, the Cold War, the AIDS epidemic, the murder of John Lennon, and the start of the Iraq—Iran war (though back then it was called the First Persian Gulf War). This was also the year that Mount St. Helens erupted and a heat wave killed over 1,250 people across the United States.

It was a tough year. And it made a perfect storm for the impact that The Police—and more specifically that song—had on people. For lots of Americans, *Zenyatta Mondatta* felt like clarity in a decade that felt more and more chaotic.

That song stayed with me through high school, through college, and into my career as a successful marketer. Decades later, when I asked myself questions like "What makes a sale?" or "What is good marketing?" I wondered how The Police had crafted a phrase that hit me like a wet salmon across the face. How had they written a song that millions of Americans connected with on a deeply individual level?

What if you could present information—any information, to any person—in a way that impacted people like a hit single can?

What if learning was easy?

What if teaching was easy?

What if communicating anything could be easy?

Let's say you need to present an idea you've been laboring over for months. Maybe it's a proposal for a client, a job description, a new concept in the classroom, a sales pitch, or a plea to convince your teenager to make better decisions. Whomever the audience, at the end of your presentation, you're expecting something. What is that something?

If you are like the rest of us, you might want your audience to engage with the new information in a way that leads to choices and actions that comply somewhat with that new knowledge. Essentially, whenever we present information, we hope for a change in audience behavior. We also want people to appreciate the time and effort we spent, and to walk away with something valuable that will be useful to them in their world.

But how often do we spend hours preparing a presentation knowing full well that the nuggets of information will fall on deaf ears, dissipate over their heads, or just won't connect?

Think about the last time you trained an employee, offered a pitch, or just had a conversation with a friend. Did you see a change afterward? Did your audience even remember the main point? How often do you feel like you're looking at Homer Simpson staring into space, replete with a conversation bubble featuring a monkey slamming a pair of cymbals? Multitudes of studies show that when information is presented in a typical classroom environment, almost everyone forgets more than 80% of the content in less than *one hour*.[1]

I wondered, *If people only retain about 20% of information, why do I still know every line of that song, decades later?* Most importantly, *Can I present information the way a hit single can?*

To answer those questions, I needed a cognitive learning neuroscientist.

Kieran's Story

In 1981, I found myself back in academia...again. I had just ended a 10-year career teaching science and social studies at an inner city all-boys high school. I left because I was desperately seeking solutions to large philosophical questions that seemed to evolve into daily crises in my classrooms.

> Why were some kids showing up as if they were meant to be at the bottom of the totem pole?
>
> Why were we labeling and stratifying children the moment they arrived in school?
>
> Did we do this based on where they came from, as if their zip code had a hidden meaning?

In the faculty room, we spoke in forward-looking platitudes and used phrases like "equality of educational opportunity." But I could see quite plainly that neither "equality" nor "opportunity" was associated with the education we were doling out. I felt like I was part of a stratification engine that unintentionally and unknowingly did bad things to young people every day.

After a horrible event at school, I arrived in Seattle wondering, *How could a 13-year-old become so dissatisfied with life at school and home that the only choice left was suicide?*

It took me the best part of 40 years to locate the solution. The journey that contributed to this book involved many dead ends for me, as well as unfortunate and time-consuming false starts and frustrating educational misadventures in academia.

But eventually, it led me to the cognitive learning model in this book, and to Rich Carr.

The pedagogic model and the brain-enabled methodologies described in *Brain-centric Design* are meant for educators in every field of learning, including instructional designers, corporate trainers, teachers, salespeople, and parents. It is useful for anyone who wants to convey information effectively. It turns out that knowledge about how the human brain works and how people learn illuminates a space that is personal to all of us and paradoxically universal as well.

The Cognitive Revolutions You May Have Missed

Homo sapiens is eminently hardwired to learn and subsequently hardwired to teach. Our species has been learning and adapting for hundreds of thousands of years—after all, we are the survivors. Our near relatives, *Homo erectus*, *Australopithecus africanus*, and *Homo neanderthalensis* didn't make it—in fact, all fell by the wayside (more than likely by our hands).

Our incredible capacity to think, create, adapt, and learn endowed us with the evolutionary advantages necessary to become one of the most successful organisms on the planet.

We can trace *Homo sapiens* cognition back 30,000 years to the Chauvet Cave in southern France. In this remote location, the first cognitive revolution we know of took place when an inventive ancestral thinker made an immortal mark by forcibly spitting a mouthful of red ochre (a mixture of mud and paint) onto their outstretched hand, which was placed high on the wall. On that day, some unknown cognitivist said, "I'm here and I want to create." Since our ancestor painted the first abstraction known to humanity, the worlds of creativity, invention, and survival have remained indelibly intertwined.

From that historic trajectory in the Chauvet Cave, many ordinary events have led to extraordinary breakthroughs and advances. It's as if humankind suddenly arrives at a leaping-off place, where we experience a "red ochre moment" that changes life as we know it.

For educators, our present times have the potential to be such a moment. Today, scientists of all genres have amassed an astounding body of work that has the power to once again transform the way we teach and learn. We have the information and methodology that teachers, trainers, designers, parents, and scholars need in order to apply the neuroscience of learning to everyday activities. And it has the power to forever improve the way we raise our children, teach in schools, and train new hires.

You are likely wondering, if we have the resources to learn and teach more effectively, why aren't we doing so?

Another cognitive revolution you likely have never heard of occurred in the mid-1950s, right here in the United States.[2] In the '50s, educators and scientists in distinct fields such as psychology, anthropology, and computer science searched for a better way to teach and learn. They were convinced there were better models than the reward-punishment methods currently in use. (More on that later.)

The answers to their questions had an enormous impact in the fields of computer science, systems information, and neuroscience. Devastatingly, the world of education and learning glossed over this research, so that if you blinked, you missed the whole revolution.

Perhaps these scientists and classroom educators were too siloed in their respective fields, and too distant from each other's worlds, to reach out to one another. Or maybe educators were distracted by something else. While the cognitive revolution was in full swing, educators convinced themselves that better, faster technology would produce a new era of better, faster learners.

In some ways, technology lived up to the hype. You now have the culmination of collective human knowledge in the palm of your hand. You can "know" anything as quickly as you can type it into a search engine. But ask anyone who presents information whether technology has solved any learning issues and the answer is likely "No."

We've been hoodwinked. Bamboozled. Generally speaking, most of us aren't learning any faster than someone who lived 100 years ago. While we can recite information as quickly as our wireless connection allows, we aren't retaining any more knowledge than people were at the start of the tech revolution.

What's more, we aren't any better at conveying information either. Educators encounter the same roadblocks as people did five decades ago. Teaching isn't any easier. Learning isn't any easier. Training a new hire isn't any faster. Presentations aren't any more effective. According to many frontline teachers, the amount of information available—paired with an audience tied at the umbilical to their devices—actually makes educating *more* difficult. Not to mention, expectations are higher than ever before in today's fast-paced, tech-enabled environment.

In some respects, all that technology has allowed us to do is move the bullet point list from the chalkboard to the smart board. That's because although the limits on technology have lessened, the limits on cognitive ability remain the same. Institutions that must present information (in any shape or form) still try to teach the very same kinds of people with the very same kind of brains that educators have always been teaching. They have neural structures with the same potential and the same restrictions. The overriding function of the neural learning coping mechanism is still to prune away unused knowledge. Building neural circuitry still takes effort and intentional practice. Indeed, most learners still go through their days in what we call an "amygdala hijack," with the result being that they forget the information just as quickly as someone has taught it.

Odds are that you more or less use the same method of presenting information that Aristotle used 2,000 years ago when he lectured at the Lyceum. The classroom hasn't changed much since that time. You've sat through thousands of hours of classes and programs, so you know how this method works. You can play that role. It's the role of a single presenter, shuffling up to a lectern. Their bullet-pointed presentation is blown up behind them, lighting up the faces of a captive audience. For many of these participants, an actual monkey slamming two cymbals against their ears would be preferable.

Teach The Way People Love To Learn

From your parents to your teachers to your bosses, it's likely that every instructor you've ever known is completely unaware of a better method of teaching. By the end of this book, you might be upset about that. That's because traditional methods don't work with your brain. They raise stress levels, destroy natural curiosity, and make it difficult to recall information.

John Medina, a developmental molecular biologist and author, succinctly writes to the frustration of the matter. He states, "If you wanted to create an education environment that was directly opposed to what the brain was good at doing, you probably would design something like a classroom. If you wanted to create a business environment that was directly opposed to what the brain was good at doing, you probably would design something like a cubicle. And if you wanted to change things, you might have to tear down both and start over."[3] If you're lucky, you can scrape by teaching with traditional models. If you're unlucky, they zap your audience's desire to learn.

And that's a real problem, because people love to learn. Everyone's brain is hardwired to release chemicals that make us feel good every time we acquire new knowledge.

Of course, content is important. You love to learn the kinds of things that directly affect you. You want to learn how to perform a skill—whether it's a job, team roping, or cooking—competently and efficiently. You want to know what will make you better, faster, or stronger at whatever it is you're passionate about. You want to be smarter. You want to acquire knowledge that is life-altering, security-inducing, truth-detecting, and freedom-enabling.

(If we missed your appositive phrase, just say it out loud, right now. Then we know we have your attention. Seriously, say it out loud!)

Cognition—you're designed to want more of it, and most importantly, whomever you present to wants more as well. Yet when was the last time your audience retained every bit of information from your lecture? Has your audience ever spaced out during a presentation, even when you know they care deeply about the subject matter? On the flip side, can you remember anything from high school biology? Have you ever enjoyed being onboarded as a new hire?

It's not your fault, either as an educator or a learner. Our brains are designed to survive, meaning that they will focus on whatever is the most exciting. If Mr. Hand is lecturing about United States–Cuba relations, and the audience isn't in any way affected by the conversation, they won't be able to engage. Their minds will drift. They might doodle, they might crave pizza, but almost certainly they'll forget what was just said.

We know you recognize that behavior on both sides of the aisle. We've all experienced it.

If you like, you can compare traditional teaching methods (demonstrated by Mr. Hand) to superstitions like "Don't swim for thirty minutes after you eat or you'll cramp" or "If you pull out a gray hair, two more will pop up in its place." These anecdotal, pseudo-science filaments of yarn are seldom correct. If there is some coincidental truth to them, it's rarely because of the reason assumed.

When it comes to education in any form, traditional methods sometimes produce positive outcomes for people who are naturally compliant. The rest of us aren't as lucky. Suddenly it makes sense that one approach for teaching works for some, while other methods don't work at all. Traditional methods are fraught with frustration—especially when it comes to their alignment with how the brain processes information.

Change Mr. Hand's lecture to a field trip about kayaking, and the response would likely be, "We're in! We see a benefit for us. That's a class we can not only survive, but we'll also show up early for." It's easy to imagine the sunshine, a cool breeze, fast rapids, a little maneuvering competition between friendly conversations, the smell of river water meeting vegetation, and a healthy dose of Mother Nature. Kayaking has our full attention.

The paragraph above is engineered to align with your brain. It intentionally transported you into a kayak (willingly or not) where you felt the sun on your face and the splashing mist of the rapids, and you maneuvered the paddles in your hands while smiling, with your buddy nearby.

After reading this book, you'll be able to pick out the Big Idea and several scaffolding constructs, and you'll recognize

Multiple Perspectives in the text. You'll notice we avoided putting you into an amygdala hijack, by shying away from difficult concepts, boring explanations, or monotonous, long-winded claptrap. Instead, we invited you into a world that you recognize, where you might have memories of good experiences, so that you remain firmly in your executive function in your frontal lobe.

As you'll learn, if you dislike kayaking or fear rough water, we totally failed to keep you in your prefrontal cortex and might have unintentionally routed information to your hindbrain. Such is the challenge and opportunity with paragraph writing as opposed to kayaking.

Once you learn the BcD method, you'll be able to quickly and easily bring someone—anyone—to the point of deep understanding with a few simple structures and practices. The content that works with this framework is limitless.

Imagine if you were guaranteed a successful outcome for all the situations below...

- Selling a home in exchange for $523,000
- Teaching an equation to arrive at a sum
- Marketing to create action
- Presenting for higher engagement and scoring
- Bringing consumers to your event
- Changing a process at work to increase return on investment
- Convincing your child not to drive drunk

Brain-centric Design is a proven neuroscience method for presenting information—any information—for complete comprehension and deep understanding.

Deep understanding is critical to what we do. It is common for someone to assume they know something, only to be surprised that when asked, they can't fully explain it. Often our grasp is superficial. Once an educator uses BcD to help a learner engage with a topic or concept, they will see firsthand the difference between surface knowledge and deep understanding.

Teach For Deep Understanding

If traditional methods are hit-and-mostly-miss, then brain-aligned methods are sharpshooters. BcD consistently delivers in Fortune 100 companies, in Silicon Valley, in agricultural applications, and in game-changing cognitive strategies in classrooms across the globe, both in schools and business learning. All kinds of corporations have been suc-cessful with this method. Industry leaders in high-stakes engineering (such as aerospace and auto), international banking organizations, large-scale medical and health facilities, global retail and manufacturing icons, K–12 schools, and even mom-and-pop shops see huge benefit from this methodology. We've even used BcD with a large manufacturer to help highly specialized and trained engineers completely relearn their jobs within *months*. After working with us and using BcD, both trainees and trainers end up liking their positions more.

We've gone into call centers and reduced attrition to *zero* within the first 12 months. That's because when we present, learners retain the information. With BcD, nothing is forgotten, because learners are invited to think critically about their position, enabled to transform from a routine expert to an adaptive expert, engaged to adopt a growth mindset, and helped to understand enough to know where to find the answers they need.

BcD facilitators and Brain-centric Instructional Designers (BcIDs) have helped trainers take new hires who were just starting to meet their target performance goals in 18 months and reduced that to **12 days**. That isn't a typo. But the best news for the corporate execs who have contracted BcD teams is their improved bottom line, which often begins with BcD "self-funding" engagements—the savings in budgeted time pays for the corrective action to cognitive training. We've found the time spent learning and applying BcD pays for itself many times over.

The BcD method produces astounding results because it is the culmination of decades of peer-reviewed research in the areas of cognition and psychology, and aligns learning with how the human brain works. It bridges the gap between education and neuroscience to provide a **plan that works for every single learner, every single time**.

These results aren't surprising…at least not to us. Many corporations employ training that is too long, inefficient, and only partially successful. On the ground, that translates into preventable mistakes, a large number of retakes, time lost being unproductive, and high attrition rates. All these items are excruciatingly expensive, so it is no wonder that training and development departments have a bad rep.

In retrospect, it's easy to predict that using a model of teaching that delivers information the way the brain likes to receive it would produce results. That's because this isn't guesswork. It's not based on anecdotal evidence or a gut feeling.

It's not clever…it's science.

BcD delivers these results by inviting new learners to become cocreators of the learning space as "intelligent novices." An intelligent novice understands the content well enough to ask complex, focused questions. Their ability to produce meaningful queries places them on the road to becoming critical thinkers. BcD encourages them to actively problem-solve every step of the way.

Facilitators who are successful with this method have reported that learners who are typically recalcitrant, disruptive, or unable to give their full focus to the work are often the first to engage with the material. At the same time, learners who are usually soft-spoken and quiet find their voice, feeling confident enough to speak out and take charge of their learning.

BcD is more than a tool. It is a way of structuring a thinking process so that large quantities of information are rendered accessible through easy, digestible chunks that make sense. What's more, BcD mitigates cognitive overload and facilitates the understanding of new material. Your content remains the same—BcD simply gives you the principles, methods, insights, and key resources to adapt it to a learning paradigm that works for all learners. In addition, BcD cultivates an active professional learning community that shepherds the changing face of your information over time. In other words, it's adaptable. No matter the structural changes inside the organization, regardless of management issues that are outside your control, and whether the information presented undergoes dramatic change, BcD will always work.

At times, we hear initial disbelief about this methodology from teachers, corporate trainers, and parents. They say, "If you knew the kinds of students I was tasked to teach, you would never suggest this kind of methodology." But a few weeks later, they show up with a very different message: "How could we have missed this for so long?"

It's true. People are doubtful at the prospect of shifting from a traditional way of learning (the way it always has been) to a brain-aligned and magnificently simpler way. Why the mistrust? Why the hesitancy?

In actuality, we shouldn't be alarmed by their reaction. They act exactly the way our brains are designed to behave. If something is unfamiliar, our brains grow new structures before they can accommodate the new method. But guess what—as soon as the structures are built, we never go back.

People have a hard time believing that learning can be fun. Teachers often think that their classrooms will become too boisterous or out-of-control if the students are too excited. Some trainers worry that the class will take too much effort on their part. They are always surprised that the learners quickly assume control over their own learning, in essence making their jobs easier.

We also hear objections like, "We have way too much content and too little time to use BcD!" On the contrary, BcD immediately cuts down time to market—usually by more than 50%. Educators from all industries report that their learners learn more—at a faster rate and with astounding retention.

In early 2019, we installed BcD within a Fortune 50 company, and their traditional 14-week training course was shortened to just over 7 weeks. Before BcD, attrition rates were high. After BcD, trainees were promoted to top positions and fell in love with their jobs, and attrition naturally disappeared. With thousands of trainees per year costing the business tens of thousands of dollars each to train (and you must multiply that further if you factor in rehiring and retraining globally), the business now saves millions every year. Not only are there huge cost savings, but its customers are served much more efficiently and effectively.

How To Read This Book

As you read, you'll get all the science without the long white jackets and questionable probes. You'll indulge in a meaningful academic investigation into how you learn at a cognitive level. You're not going to learn everything about the brain—only the parts that impact learning, or what we call "sexy brain bits." You'll learn helpful and interesting facts about teaching and learning, with the help of the BcD characters below, and enjoy periodic brain breaks, which will give you a new activity to focus on and also illustrate one of the key principles of BcD learning.

Soon you'll be able to take any information you present and make it better. What's more, you'll be able to present it in less time, and your audience will enjoy being a part of it. There will be no more burnout from cognitive overload or stress from too much material to cover in too little time, and you will eliminate that egregious distraction to all learning—the infamous tyranny of the textbook. You can steer clear of other fallacies of mass learning, where mile-wide, inch-deep landscapes are exposed for what they are—outdated and overvalued.

Instead, you'll revel in a structure you can't unlearn and experience the fulfillment of your method's effectiveness. Imagine your clients, prospects, students, manager, or children learning information and deeply understanding it with the same eagerness and excitement of listening to a hit single. Envision them actively thinking and collaborating about your material, without any prompting, threatening, cajoling, or begging on your end. They will see benefit in your information and internalize it as their own.

Much more than a set of tips for educators, BcD is a teaching framework that aligns with how the brain accepts new information and how people love to learn. It is intuitive and easy, and will forever transform the way you present information. It will likely alter the way you view learning, intelligence, and the brain. It may even positively impact the way you treat yourself and others.

Welcome to our world. You're about to explore *Brain-centric Design: The Surprising Neuroscience Behind Learning with Deep Understanding.*

PART I

Your Brain: Demystify Three Pounds Of Goop

1.1

Learning Is Connecting The Dots

To run, you need legs. To shop, you need currency. To cook, you need ingredients.

To learn, you need neurons.

To teach, you need to know how neurons work.

You can appreciate what your neurons do for you by focusing on your big toe. Specifically, the sensation that occurs between your big toe and the inside of your sock. You're so adept at it, you can even remember which pair of socks you put on this morning. Yet you didn't notice your toe a few seconds ago, before reading the first sentence. How did you suddenly become aware of it?

It's not magic; it's neurons.

Of course, your neurons could always feel your toe, even before you brought your attention to it. It isn't like it was separated from your body until you remembered it was there. You didn't experience the sensation because a collection of neurons decided it was unimportant.

To answer the simple question "Which socks did I put on this morning?" billions of electrical impulses pass through billions of neurons that span from the top of your head to the tip of your toes. For you to feel your sock, each neuron must communicate successfully with the next. If for some traumatic reason the connection was interrupted, you'd be terrified, and you'd wonder where your big toe went.

3

If the neural circuitry to your big toe was interrupted and you lost sensation, there is a chance that in the future, you could regain feeling. As you'll learn, I am incredibly malleable. I can compensate for broken connections and misaligned firings by building new circuitry. Similar to survivors who regain speech after a traumatic brain injury or veterans who adjust to artificial limbs, I can make miraculous recoveries.

If you wiggle your toes, the sensation changes. Go ahead, try it! There is an incredible intricacy in that one instant. It's a moment teeming with billions of charged neurons firing and connecting almost instantaneously, wiring to light up a brilliant network, communicating at unimaginable speeds—just so that you can wonder which sock you picked out of the drawer today.

The speed of neural communication varies depending on what information is being communicated and where that communication is coming from. But in the case of the spinal cord, we know that signals can travel up to 268 miles per hour—the fastest transmission in the human body. However, areas that lack myelination (like receptors in the skin) can be as slow as one mile per hour.

To carry out complex tasks like wiggling your toes, your brain must connect the dots—or neurons—to make that happen. All of those connections form to create the most truly

amazing structure in your body. Michio Kaku (the mind behind
string theory) once said that the human brain is the most complex thing we have yet discovered in our universe.[1] It's easy to
see why. Your brain is made up of somewhere between 85 and
100 *billion* neurons.

What does 100 billion actually *look* like? Let's stack some
dollar bills.

- A single dollar bill measures .0043 inches high.

- A pile of 100 dollar bills measures .43 inches high.

- A pile of 1,000 dollar bills measures 4.3 inches high.

- A pile of 1,000,000 (1 million) dollar bills measures
  4,300 inches, or 358 feet, about the height of a 30-to
  35-story building.

- 100,000,000 (100 million) dollar bills measures 35,851
  feet, or 6.79 miles. This would reach from the Earth's
  surface to the approximate altitude at which commercial
  jets fly.

- A stack of 1,000,000,000 (1 billion) dollar bills measures
  358,510 feet, or 67.9 miles. They would reach from the
  Earth's surface into the lower portion of the tropo-
  sphere, one of our major atmospheric layers.

- And a stack of 100,000,000,000 (100 billion) dollar bills
  measures 6,786.6 miles. A column of bills this high
  would extend 28 times higher than the orbiting International Space Station.[2]

If the number 100 billion seems large, consider that each neuron can have up to 10,000 connections. Imagine 100 billion neurons working together as a team to form hundreds of *trillions* of connections. If those connections were a stack of dollar bills, they'd reach to the moon and back 14 times! Think of the possible combinations and permutations—it's a mathematical playground. The numbers are astronomical, like all of the stars and planets that make up the Milky Way...times 1,000. All this complexity, a multidimensional web of intersecting neurons, forms one of the most beautifully intricate systems known to humankind—all compacted into a three-pound organic mass of goop that sits inside your skull.

Einstein spent the last part of his life trying to find a "theory of everything," or one that could tie together his theory of general relativity and quantum mechanics, which at the time were not fully compatible. As physicists picked up where Einstein left off, one solution was string theory. String theory combines the two theories by assuming there are multiple universes and dimensions beyond the ones we know.

While the brain is admittedly complex, the individual parts of the neuron are easy to understand. Like most cells, neurons consist of a cell body and a nucleus. Like the skin cells on the back of your hand and the plant cells in your philodendron, they house DNA and all the little organelles responsible for homeostasis (regulation) in the cell. Unlike other cells, neurons have several specialized parts that facilitate communication between other neurons. These consist of axons, axon terminals, myelin sheaths, and brain fibers called dendrites.

We often refer to sections of the brain "lighting up" when they activate. That's because neuroscientists measure brain activity with something called functional magnetic resonance imaging (fMRI). An fMRI measures brain activity by detecting changes in blood flow. When one region of the brain engages, it increases blood flow to that region. The extra blood flow translates to an image on screen that displays a color, hence lighting up the region.[3] [4]

When you wiggle your toes, neurons communicate with each other using electricity and chemicals. Information is passed from neuron to neuron through an electric charge called an **action potential**. An action potential moves electricity away from the nucleus and sends it down the axon. How far that signal has to go depends—axon communication varies in length from a fraction of a centimeter (when they are communicating with a neuron next door) to a string of neurons several meters long (like when your brain sends messages to your big toe). Once the signal reaches the end of the axon, it enters the axon terminals, which can have as many as 10,000 branches spread out toward the corresponding dendrites of other neurons.

At the axon terminal, the electrical signal undergoes an interesting change. As you can see in the following illustration, each neuron is separated from every other neuron by an empty space called a **synapse**. Counterintuitively, although this space is a physical separation, neuroscientists think of it as a connection point between the two neurons. The space is small, between 20–40 nanometers wide. To put this into perspective, a single sheet of standard printer paper is typically 100,000 nanometers wide.

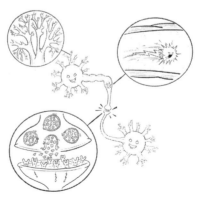

Through a complex chemical process, the action potential in Neuron A changes into a neurotransmitter, which is kicked out across the synapse between neurons. Dendrites from Neuron B act as receptors and transform the chemical message back into an electric charge that will help create a new action potential. Neuron B can either transmit the action potential on to Neuron C or it can quiet (inhibit) the message and keep it from transmitting further. If the action potential is strong enough, the electric signal moves to more and more neurons.

When an action potential is spread between neurons, your dendrites grow. More accurately, your dendritic spines increase in number and size from electrical stimulation, leading to something called **dendritic arborization.**

Growing dendrites is kind of like growing Christmas trees. Consider Charlie Brown's tree—it's wimpy, sparse, and rather pathetic. Then compare that to the Christmas tree at Rockefeller Center. That one is lavishly decorated with thousands of glowing lights, tinsel, and ornaments. It is so beautiful, it receives national attention every year. Dendrites are similar in that they can be sparse or amazingly lush.

Dendrites are outcomes of activity-dependent plasticity. In other words, under normal conditions, their size can change in response to how often they are used. Long-term depression (lack of stimulation) results in abnormalities and cognitive challenges, while long-term potentiation (lots of stimulation) results in spines that are larger and healthier.

Not only do your dendrites grow in size and plumage through increased use, they also expand by connecting to axons of other neurons over and over. This kind of cognitive rehearsal or repetition is exactly how arborization helps you learn. This is referred to as synaptic potentiation or sprouting, where activation causes thick growth.

On the opposite side, when less activation occurs (reduced usage) dendrites are pruned away in a process called synaptic depression. The more cells they connect to, the larger your dendritic branching patterns. This is important because typically the more connections, the greater the processing power and storage capacity in your brain.

In general, the more often an action potential is passed between the same group of neurons, the greater the dendritic arborization of each neuron. Just like the more water and nutrients you give a plant, the deeper the roots grow…the more synapses that fire between neurons, the more brain fibers grow. In this way, dendrites grow **spiny arbors** as you acquire and make meaning out of information.

Aha moments occur when a new neural pathway is created between existing circuitry and new knowledge. Remember the first time you understood a tricky physics equation or the meaning of a line of poetry? How about the first time you opened the hood of a car or fixed a flat tire on a bicycle? That aha moment accompanied what we call "making visible" the connection between prior knowledge and new information, which you somehow used to make sense of the difficult concept. Before the learning event, you could read the poetry and could see the bicycle tire. The solution to the equation was always the same. Yet for whatever reason, on that particular day, a trigger caused several disparate bits of knowledge to make a connection, and you understood how and why you arrived at the conclusion.

If you decide you enjoy analyzing poetry or fixing cars, the message that contributed to the aha moment will repeatedly travel between neurons, its dendritic arborization will grow, and eventually it will create or contribute to a **neural circuit**.

1.2

Insulate Your Neurons

Repetition of a thought eventually creates a neural circuit. You strengthen and build these neural circuits through an amazing process called **myelination**.

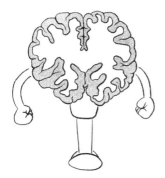

Myelinated neuronal connections are referred to as "white matter" because they appear white in comparison to the billions of neurons, which appear as "gray matter."

Myelin is a white, fatty substance that speeds up the brain's ability to take in, manage, and process information. Recall that an electric impulse moves down the axon from the neuron's cell body. Myelin wraps around the axon, acting like insulating tape for this electrical charge, ensuring that it makes it all the way to the axon terminals at the end.

Myelinated circuits are incredibly efficient. The electrical impulse can travel from node to node up to 40 times faster in a myelinated circuit in comparison to traveling the length of an unmyelinated axon. In terms of speed, comparing myelinated and unmyelinated neurons is like comparing a Formula One race car to your granddad's John Deere tractor. In fact, speeds of more than 200 miles per hour have been observed. Myelination matters even more when you consider that some axon communications (like between the brain and the big toe) are as long as the human body. For the brain to achieve the same level of efficiency without myelination, the spinal cord would have to be *three yards* in diameter, about as long as a standard couch is wide.

To see firsthand how myelinated circuitry speeds up neural pathways, go visit a ranch. There you'll notice something incredible about newborn animals like lambs, calves, and foals. Unlike a human infant, at birth, a foal can stand up and walk, even if wobbly at first. They are almost immediately endowed with enough strength and coordination to survive in the wild.

After eight short hours, a foal can even *run* if it has to.[1] So why does it take a human infant between 9 and 12 months to take a few measly steps? The foal is hardwired for survival. It is born with almost all of the neural circuitry that is required to run *already* connected and myelinated. Those connections grow stronger as the foal matures, but for all intents and purposes, it comes out of the womb running. On the other hand, while an infant has all the neurons they need to become proficient at walking, running, and jumping, those neurons are not yet connected or myelinated. The child crawls, struggles to get up, falls down hundreds of times, and eventually grows neural circuitry that supports elementary mobility. Through hours of practice, some intentional and some involuntary, the circuitry eventually myelinates, and the child walks with ease.

1.3

Get To Know Your Sexy Brain Bits

The neurons that make up your brain work together to create specific structures and regions that are categorized based on localized mental function. These structures are like behind-the-scenes engineers on a movie set. At a very basic level, there are three main regions in your brain:

- Hindbrain
- Midbrain
- Forebrain

The **hindbrain** receives a lot of attention in popular culture and is commonly referred to as the "reptilian" or "animal" brain. It is responsible for most of the functions that keep you alive, such as controlling your heartbeat and breathing. It is also commonly referred to as the "ancient" or "primitive" brain, in that it was one of the

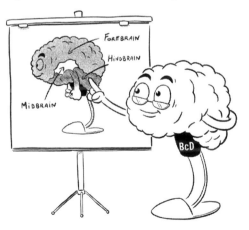

The **midbrain** connects the hindbrain and the forebrain. It is associated with motor control, vision, hearing, temperature regulation, and alertness.

earliest parts to evolve. We share the structures in the hindbrain with most other animals. Interestingly, when we are born and our bodies mature, the hindbrain is one of the first parts to wire and myelinate.

The **forebrain** is separated into two hemispheres: the left and the right. Separating the two hemispheres is a highly myelinated region known as the corpus callosum. The **corpus callosum** mediates information between the left and right hemispheres at very fast speeds. In doing so, it helps us process sensory inputs from the outside environment. When the corpus callosum is severed intentionally (usually to reduce or inhibit life-threatening epileptic seizures), patients report that

Interestingly, for people with a severed corpus callosum, it is possible to have a well-developed language center in both hemispheres. This means that it is humanly possible to read two pages of a book at the same time and recall information from both pages. The bad news is that since the two hemispheres are unable to communicate, you might end up with a split personality. When this happens, actions performed by either hemisphere can go unnoticed by the other. Imagine dating a person with this personality type!

it creates the sensation of two separate people living in the same head. Through research on these patients, scientists were able to show that each hemisphere is indeed responsible for different functions.[1]

The brain can further be sectioned into six major regions based on function.

	Brain Stem Top of spine	• Receives sensory data • Controls lungs, heart, and blood pressure
	Cerebellum Above brain stem	• Involved in balance and executive monitoring
	Occipital Lobe Back of brain, above cerebellum	• Receives sensory data from eyes • Recognizes shapes, colors, and objects • Controls eye movements • Involved in spatial mapping

	Parietal Lobe Top of brain	• Translates sensory data from sight, sound, taste, and touch • Gives you a sense of "you"
	Temporal Lobe Divided into two hemispheres behind each ear	• Receives, recognizes, and interprets auditory information • Involved with physical hearing, speech, and interpretation
	Frontal Lobe Front of brain; forehead	• Governs personality, character, and behavior • Controls body movement • Allows planning, organizing, problem solving, predicting, thinking, and learning

The **brain stem** sits at the top of the spine. It controls your lungs, heart, and blood pressure. It also receives sensory data from the rest of your body. In some ways, your brain stem is the most important part of your body, because it performs all the background functions that keep you alive at a basic level. That's why in shows like *The Walking Dead*, this region is the only working part of the zombified brain.[2]

The **occipital lobe** is in the very back of your brain, above your cerebellum. It receives messages from your eyes and recognizes shapes, colors, and objects. This region of the brain allows you to tell the difference between a square and a triangle. It also controls your eye movements.

The visual cortex in the occipital lobe allows you to move with an understanding of the physical landscape. Visual mapping is complex, and is one of those things we generally take for granted until there is a mishap. For example, something has gone awry with your visual mapping when you think there is one extra step to a flight of stairs.

Counterintuitively, images from your left eye are processed in the right hemisphere of your occipital lobe, while images from your right eye are processed in the left. This is called "crossing the midline" or **decussation**. Evolutionary biologists argue that decussation emerged in response to distinct physiological and anatomical constraints. For example, imagine if the head had been a different shape a million or so years ago. If so, the visual cortex might have been stacked one on top of the other, but over time, perhaps it evolved in response to environmental and other demands. Despite how it arose, crossing the midline is an excellent tool to employ when you feel like a learner can't possibly digest one more fact or bit of info.

Decussation is a teleological argument, meaning it "relates to or involves the explanation of phenomena in terms of the purpose they serve rather than of the cause by which they arise." Think about looking back in time and understanding that things that look strange today might have served a purpose in the past in a different place, and over time they just happened to fall where they are today and they still work.

The **parietal lobe** is on the very top of your brain. Its job is to translate the messages you receive from sight, sound, taste, and touch. In other words, the parietal lobe gives you a sense of YOU. This part of the brain differentiates your body from the outside world.

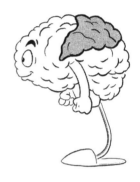

If you damage your left parietal lobe, you might experience Gerstmann's syndrome. Symptoms of Gerstmann's syndrome include left-right confusion, difficulty with writing and mathematics, language disorders, and agnosia, a condition described as an "abnormal perception of objects."[3] [4][5][6] If you damage your right parietal lobe, you might start neglecting the left side of your body. This disorder is called contralateral neglect, and it can make many self-care activities, like dressing and washing, a struggle. If you asked a contralateral neglect patient to draw a clock, they may only draw half the numbers, as they aren't aware of the other half of their visual field.[7]

Your **temporal lobe** is divided into two hemispheres, one located behind each ear. The temporal lobes have a few distinct responsibilities. They receive, recognize, and interpret auditory information that comes in through your ears. The left side focuses on physical hearing and speech, while the right side focuses on interpretation and understanding.

The **frontal lobe** is located at the very front of your brain, behind your forehead. It governs your personality, character, and behavior. It is what controls your body movement and allows you to organize and plan. It is also where you solve problems, think, and learn. It houses your prefrontal cortex, which controls your **executive function** and higher-order cognitive processes like inhibition, cognitive shifting, and **working memory**.

As we experience reality, our nervous system transmits sensory information from our five senses—sight, taste, touch, smell and sound—into our brain.

Functional neurologists have found that taste buds recognize five distinct flavors: sweet, salty, sour, bitter, and umami (roughly translated to "yummy" in Japanese, but it has been further described as savory). Astonishingly, while you have only evolved receptors for five flavors,[8] you can smell *hundreds* of different scents. Next time you pour a glass of wine, use your sense of smell to your advantage. First, breathe the wine in through your nose before drinking, then exhale as you take a sip.[9]

The **cerebellum** sits at the back of the brain just above the brain stem. It controls the body's sense of balance. It enables you to stand up, walk in a straight line, and touch your toes. It lets you know whether you're standing up or sitting down. Interestingly, although the cerebellum comprises about 10% of the total volume of your brain, it has more neurons than all the other structures in your brain combined.

For decades, neuroscientists believed that the only functions of the cerebellum were balance, motion, and control of the body's spatial movements. But in 2018, a landmark study proved that only 20% of its neurons are involved with this kind of motion management. The other 80% are dedicated to areas involved in functions such as abstract thinking, planning, emotion, memory, and language, which you've just learned takes place primarily in the frontal lobe.[10]

The cerebellum doesn't *directly* carry out tasks like thinking, just as it doesn't *directly* control movement. Instead, it appears to monitor the brain areas that are doing the work. It makes those areas perform better, acting as a kind of editor, constantly reviewing and improving your thoughts, decisions, and motor movements.

Now that we have a better understanding of the various functions of the cerebellum, it's no surprise that alcohol affects more than our balance. We finally have an explanation for all the bad ideas people have when they're drunk: they lack cerebellar editing of their thoughts. In the same vein, we now recognize why getting up out of a sedentary seated situation to do a brain break or a focused breathing exercise helps stimulate learning. The cerebellum and the prefrontal cortex are joined at the hip.

If you burned your finger on a candle, sensory information from the heat of the flame, the color of fire, and the shape of the candle transmitted from the neurons in your sensory organs. From there, it was processed by very precise regions of the brain, but generally moved from the hindbrain to the midbrain and the frontal lobes.

Remember how you pulled your finger away from the flame before you actually realized what was happening? That's because your reactionary brain—or hindbrain and midbrain—responded to the sensation before the information reached your forebrain. The fact that you reacted to the event before cognitively understanding what created the pain is a critical point in understanding how learning takes place. For learning to occur, all regions of the brain work together to make sense of the new sensation or information so that it is encoded in long-term memory. From now on, the flame will be associated with various regions that have to do with pain, smell, sound, vision, and touch.

The Importance Of Brain Breaks

Typically, learners are sitting down in classrooms as they are absorbing new information. This forces the blood to flow to the buttocks and thigh region. But for executive function, the brain needs this blood. By standing up to do a brain break, you achieve two things:

- You engage the cerebellum for balance and movement.
- You get the blood flowing in the cerebral regions.

With that in mind, let's try one now!

*   *   *

BRAIN BREAK: CROSSING THE MIDLINE

For this brain break, you need two rubber balls. You can do this exercise alone or with a group.

Start with your dominant hand and bounce the ball on that side of your body as you count to five. The louder you count, the more focus you will be able to master. After you feel confident with your dominant hand, try bouncing the ball on your other side with your less dominant hand. Again, count out loud. Once you get good at that, bounce both balls together, one on each side. When you get to the number five, attempt to receive the bouncing balls in a simple crisscross manner. In other words, bounce both balls the usual way, but after they leave your hands, switch the left over right so that you receive the right ball in the left hand and the left ball in the right hand. It is a little challenging at first, but your brain will quickly figure out what you are after.

This simple exercise is fun and counterintuitive. It is intentionally powerful for your focus, attention, and working memory.

Note: To see this brain break and others, go to www.braincentricdesign.com/brainbreak.

*   *   *

When you bounce a ball using your left hand, you activate your right hemisphere. When you do the same thing with the right hand, you activate the left hemisphere. When you cross the midline, you engage the corpus callosum and activate the whole brain. By counting out loud, you bring attentional focus to your work, and this activates the temporal lobes along with the parietal lobe for small motor skills. To monitor and manage all this activity, you are engaging the executive function of your prefrontal cortex, and when you reach proficiency with the easy stuff, simply increasing the cognitive load will keep your brain nicely tuned and challenged.

In addition, and very important for learning, you are releasing many different and powerful learning agents into your synaptic spaces when you carry out a fun brain break like this. Neurotransmitters associated with learning flood the synapses and prepare the brain for new concepts and difficult information. Dopamine, serotonin, norepinephrine, and oxytocin are systematically released for rewards, good feelings, focus, and social fun. Break breaks are highly effective for helping people learn.

As we dive further into the structures of the brain, keep in mind that it is a highly complex system. Although each structure generally performs a specific set of tasks, rarely does one work without engaging another. For example, saying that the brain stem is the only structure involved in maintaining your heartbeat is like saying that your arm is the only part of your body used to throw a baseball. While it may be the most critical and obvious, when you play catch, your legs give you balance and power, your abdominal muscles flex, and your eyes focus on a friend's mitt.

In the same way, each part of the brain works in tandem with the whole. Essentially, while each section of your brain has a distinct function, every part of it has to work together to give you memories and emotions that create your space in the world.

Furthermore, in the exciting world of neuroscience, as soon as one discovery is made, two more pop up that refine or even challenge our understanding. What was true today may not be true tomorrow. That being said—and given that we still have very little understanding about some big questions like "What is consciousness?" and "How does consciousness work?"—most neuroscientists agree that this is the first time in history that we have an accurate model of the human brain.

1.4

How Your Brain Filters Information

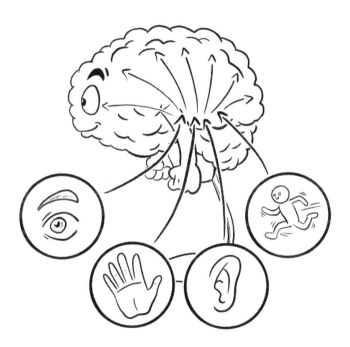

Processing information in the brain is like going on a road trip. After you hop into your car, you don't instantly reach your destination. You have to drive for a few hours. Once on the highway, you might have to stop for gas or to eat a sandwich. It takes time to get where you want to go.

Of course, when it comes to information processing in the brain, we're talking about nanoseconds, not hours, and the path taken isn't necessarily linear. In addition, the trillions of connections in the brain remind us that there are many different routes (some that we may not even be aware of yet) that we could take to get to the same destination.

Perhaps a better analogy for information processing would be hopping into your own personal spaceship and flying to any destination in spacetime.

But to simplify understanding, most scientists accept a general process to help visualize how the brain handles the billions of bits of information that enter the system every second. When you think about learning, it's helpful to imagine the information going through certain structures before reaching the frontal lobe, where your higher cognitive function takes place. Before information can get to the frontal lobe, its first stop is the reticular activating system, or RAS.

The **RAS** is a collection of neurons located in the brain stem. This system handles most information needed to administer to the needs of the physical body, like breathing, heartbeat, balance, wakefulness, and sleep. More importantly, in the context of learning, it also acts as an information filter. The RAS only allows information to pass to the frontal lobe that it (and subsequently, you) deem necessary to process with executive thinking.

Consider all the information your brain is processing at this very moment, both consciously and in the background. Your brain is reading these words, analyzing them, and learning from them. It's thinking about its RAS system and visualizing it sitting on top of your brain stem. At the same time, it's subconsciously feeling the weight of this book (or other reading device) and the texture of its pages. It's noticing the color of the words and white space between the letters.

However, your brain is doing a lot more than just focusing on what's in your hand. It's also firing neural synapses and engaging circuitry. It's gauging the temperature of the room you're sitting in and listening to the ambient noise outside. It's controlling the size of your pupils as the light changes in the room. It's digesting your last meal. It's maintaining your cardiovascular system by oxygenating your bloodstream, including the transfer of oxygen to all of your organs, the chemical and physical processes that allow that oxygen to be used by your body, and the transfer of CO_2 outside your body. It's even controlling the metabolic rate of your cells and replicating your DNA.

In case it isn't obvious, your brain is an extremely busy organ. At any point in time, it could be processing around *two million bits of data*. So how does your brain not blow a fuse like an overloaded circuit board?

The surface area of your skin is roughly 20 square feet. It houses around a million nerve cells dedicated to detecting pressure, pain, temperature, and the location of any sensation. At the same time, just one of your eyes captures more than 300 megapixels of visual information every second! Yet your conscious mind can only handle slightly more than 100 pieces of information a second. It can't even process all the visual data from one eye.[1]

As two million bits of data come in from your sensory organs, your RAS decides whether you will process that information consciously or subconsciously. Based on the type of information, the RAS will send it to the correct part of the brain for processing. It only lets what you consider to be the most important information pass through to your conscious mind for executive processing.

For example, you won't notice the noise outside on a quiet afternoon until the neighbor's dog barks, and you won't think about the temperature until you feel cold or hot. Alternately, you'll never have to balance the acidity of your stomach (although you'll notice if you have heartburn) or worry about producing enough saliva to eat (but you might salivate just thinking about lemon juice). That's because your RAS only sends information to your forebrain that needs to be processed with higher cognitive function. In simple terms, it sends information needed to keep you alive and safe in your environment.

Your RAS filter deserves your gratitude for taking over the monitoring of your heart rate and bowel movements. However, that's not all it does for you. To better appreciate how the RAS filter impacts daily life, think back to a time when you considered making a major purchase. Maybe it was a new house, a puppy, or a new car. How about a Jeep Wrangler? For weeks, you researched, read consumer reports, and compared prices. Suddenly, it occurred to you that there are a lot of Jeep Wranglers around town. They were all over the place! Had everyone and their neighbor gone out and bought one before you could? Of course not. But because you (and your executive function) were focused on Jeep Wranglers, your RAS sent that visual data to your frontal lobe.

Think back to the last time you were at a barbecue. There was a lot of sensory data to absorb. Groups of people chattered over the music in the background, and you smelled food from the grill. Cars drove by and dogs barked. There was a lot going on visually too. People shuffled in and out, partygoers scooted chairs around tables, and a slight breeze moved the leaves in the trees. You subconsciously let your RAS filter out all the information in the background, wanting to focus on what your friend said. Then, from across the room, someone uttered your name. It was in a casual tone, quiet even. Yet suddenly you couldn't hear anything aside from what was said about you. What happened? Your RAS filter passed on information that it deemed relevant. In this instance, it was gossip about you.

The RAS filter can do much more than make you aware of a specific brand of vehicle or help you focus on your name in a crowded room. It can filter complex information about your perception of yourself, like self-worth and intelligence.

For example, in elementary school, we are classified by our grade results. Letter designations such as A, B, C, D, and F are educational constructs designed to let students know which areas they are excelling in and where they are falling behind. But in reality, these constructs do more to predetermine what we will succeed and fail at than to increase proficiency across the board. When a child receives an F, how are they not supposed to think they are dumb? How many children receive a low letter grade and think, *I should spend some more time on that subject?*

This idea becomes personal when you consider your own experience in grades K-12. Rich remembers his.

When I was in school, I was the kid who couldn't concentrate during math class. Meanwhile, my friend Melissa was already stellar with algebra. Every time our tests were handed back, I was further discouraged—my test was filled with red ink while hers was nearly spotless, except for the large A+ scribbled at the top. I was convinced that I was inept and that Melissa was a genius. Her brain had to have been better than mine!

It was easy to convince myself of that idea when the evidence was all around our classroom. I could easily label the "bright" kids and the "dumb" kids—all I had to do was look at the grade they were issued. Everything seemed to reinforce the idea that some of us were born smart and others were just *not*. And it was easy to convince myself that there really wasn't much I could do to change it. Haynie always got an A in art. Woodard always got an A in physics. Some kids never got an A for anything.

As a child, I didn't understand what was happening to my brain every time I received a low grade. The more I thought *I'm bad at math*, the stronger the neural circuitry grew to reinforce that idea. And while this is a chicken-and-egg phenomenon (as in which came first), the more I focused on that idea, the stronger the neural circuitry became and vice versa.

Over time, I calibrated my RAS to focus on it more and more. Suddenly, it didn't matter that I had received an A in Spanish. I figured it was probably a fluke or that I just got lucky. The information my RAS filter was sending to my higher functions confirmed the idea that I wasn't one of the "bright" kids.

Quantum physicists today agree that the chicken and the egg happen at the same time. Let's say you're heading to work. You usually ride your bike to the building then walk up the stairs. It has to be in that order. However, at the quantum (particle) level, cause and effect aren't always linear. According to new research, this phenomenon is called "indefinite causal order," meaning that both events happen first.[2]

The standard method of teaching does not treat our brains like the infinitely brilliant circuitry that they contain. It's not that Haynie or Woodard or Melissa have better brains than other kids—they have essentially the same 100 billion neurons making connections that the rest of us have. They have the same cognitive ability as everyone else. However, if we *believe* that we are not going to be successful at math or science or Spanish or art, then it becomes a kind of self-fulfilling prophecy. Our busy neurons team up to create a neural circuit to reinforce that belief. Structures like the RAS continue to send sensory data to our higher functions to verify that belief, and the neural circuit becomes stronger. Every time we receive a poor grade or answer a question incorrectly, that belief is reinforced, and the neural circuit becomes more efficient. After a while, that letter grade has you convinced that your dreams are too big and your mind is too weak.

Thinking, as you'll soon see, is a powerful tool in learning—once you learn how to control it.

The great news is that your life doesn't have to be predetermined by a collection of neurons. On the contrary, understanding the relationship between your thoughts and the circuitry of your brain is incredibly empowering. If your thoughts and feelings are simply neurons communicating, it's clear that you can easily change those pathways. You can, with awareness and intention, calibrate your RAS to confirm positive beliefs instead of negative ones.

There are plenty of examples of people recalibrating their RAS to attain incredible results. One is the case of a professional musician who, although incredibly accomplished, still saw some areas for improvement. His third finger on his left hand was not quite as responsive as the third finger on his right hand. He had convinced himself that this finger was the problem in his musical career. He could always depend on this finger for evidence as to why he was not a brilliant musician. Having learned about intentional practice, neural circuitry, and RAS, he convinced himself that he had nothing to lose.[3] He gave it a shot.

He envisioned a mental model of neural circuits growing and myelinating for this finger. He practiced slowly and

thought about it often. He'd even practice pieces of music on the steering wheel of his car, all while imagining his finger building faster, better circuitry. Nothing happened for a week or so. Then one evening as he was playing a rather difficult piece, he was shocked. Not only did his finger leap at the occasion, but it performed flawlessly for the first time in his life. Being cynical, he thought, *No way...that was a fluke. That won't ever happen again!*

Today, he's had such incredible results with his ring finger that he's moved on to his pinkies. He is now convinced that any finger can improve with effort and time.

If we convince ourselves that we are going to solve an algebraic equation or speak a foreign language, our neurons will busy themselves building neural circuits around this positive belief, which greatly increases the odds that we will achieve the goal. While simply believing we can accomplish something won't instantly provide us with the skill set needed, it will form a positive association with the topic.

When we perceive something as positive or enjoyable, our RAS filter will provide evidence to support our belief. The more evidence we find that suggests we can acquire a skill, the more likely we are to continue to struggle to gain that skill. Or in neural terms, we are more likely to engage in the repetitive activity that increases the neural circuitry needed to perform that skill.

In other words, having a mental model of how the RAS filters information and aids in building circuitry gives us an astonishing amount of control over just how successful we are in the pursuit of certain skills, concepts, and knowledge.

1.5

Google Is Like Your Hippocampus

The hippocampi are situated in the temporal lobes of the brain. As you may recall, the temporal lobes reside in both hemispheres of the cerebral structure. We refer to both hippocampi collectively as the hippocampus. The hippocampus is closely aligned with learning, memory, and **spatial mapping**. Short-term memory is processed here and, over time, memories are consolidated and distributed to the outer cerebral cortex.

The hippocampus is similar to a search engine such as Google. When someone creates a webpage, Google indexes and stores that page. When someone searches the keywords on that webpage, Google retrieves it. It also prioritizes webpages that have the most activity and buries those with little activity.

Similarly, the hippocampus sends memories out to the appropriate part of the cerebral cortex for long-term storage and then retrieves them when triggered. Like Google, it prioritizes whatever information is used the most. That's why it's easier to recall information that you think about often. For example, it might be easier to remember the processes involved with your current job as opposed to the job you had in high school, even though the tasks you currently perform are likely more complex. That's also why it's easier to recall what you had for breakfast this morning rather than what you ate last Tuesday.

Of course, like everything that happens in your brain, memory is complicated. If something happened Tuesday to make that breakfast memorable, like while eating you saw your pet rabbit get chased by a bald eagle, or a cousin you didn't even know you had knocked on your front door, you'd probably remember it with clarity. That's because you've tied an emotional and unusual element of novelty to your bacon and eggs.

The example above shows how **recency** and **primacy** seem to dictate your capacity to retrieve information—unless you are intentional about how you encode it. If you or a friend are particularly savvy at memorizing names, it's likely not because they have a special gift. Instead, they probably use common tricks (whether they are aware of it or not) to help them be intentional about how they encode those names into their hippocampus.

Memory methods include focusing on a unique feature of their face, turning their name into a rhyme, associating them with a particular event, or making an acronym (like ROYGBIV for the colors of the spectrum). For example, a common rhyme used to identify one of the deadly serpents in North America, the coral snake, is "Red touch yellow, kill a fellow; red touch black, friend of Jack."

The hippocampus has multiple functions beyond memory. It also aids in our capacity for spatial mapping, or our ability to understand where we are in relation to other objects. Spatial mapping allows us to navigate. Some people think they have a sixth sense when they are turning in the right direction. It turns out, it's actually just a well-developed hippocampus. On the other hand, people who have failures in the hippocampal regions (like those with Alzheimer's disease) suffer from chronic loss of short-term memory and serious disorientation.

To understand just how critical the hippocampus is to learning and memory, meet Henry. If you bumped into Henry in the produce section of a grocery store, he would be happy to meet you. If you reached for some lettuce and bumped into him again, he'd be happy to meet you *again*. By the time you both reached the deli, Henry would have no recollection of ever having met you in the first place.

Henry, referred to by his initials (HM) until after his death, became one of the most famous patients in medical history, because his particular malady (and the remedy attempted) produced a valuable trove of evidence that helped scientists better understand the role of the hippocampus and the formation of new memories.

In the early 1950s, HM signed up for a surgery that he hoped would cure his epilepsy. At that point in history, it was rare for an experimental surgery of this nature to be conducted on a human. It was too risky, even irresponsible. However, HM wasn't responding to anticonvulsive medication, and his brain had deteriorated to the point that without drastic action, he would likely die from his episodes. Surgeons knew from animal studies that removal of one of the hippocampi helped relieve symptoms of convulsion during an epileptic fit, so they hypothesized that the same would be true of humans. HM was the first person brave (and desperate) enough to try.

Surgeons originally planned to remove just one of his hippocampi but decided that HM's epilepsy was so severe that they should remove both. On September 1, 1953, he underwent a bilateral medial temporal lobectomy to remove the anterior two-thirds of his hippocampi. The result surprised everyone.

In some respects, the surgery was a resounding success. HM's epileptic episodes decreased considerably, and he was able to live out the rest of his life until passing at age 72. However, in a way the surgery was also a tragedy, because HM lost the mechanism for converting short-term memory into long-term memory and the capacity to make new memories. He suffered from surgery-induced anterograde amnesia—a complete inability to recall the recent past. HM lived the rest of his life in a permanent Groundhog Day.

An extraordinary discovery followed some initial investigation about HM's case. It turns out that while HM could not create new memories, if he went back far enough (in his case, about 10 years), he could retrieve old memories.[1] From this observation, scientists made two important discoveries related to memory. First, they learned that the hippocampus is involved in the formation of new memories. Second, they learned that after a number of years, memories are encoded in long-term memory storage somewhere other than the hippocampus. Scientists were beginning to understand just how complicated memory is.

Interestingly, too much memory can be just as difficult as too little. In healthy humans, memory is not a video recorder. I can forget things that are unimportant to me, and I can soften bad memories. I can even block a traumatic event entirely. Individuals with hyperthymesia do not have this ability. They can recall almost every day of their lives in near perfect detail. Those affected describe their condition as a nightmare. Recollection of their memories is uncontrollable. Any sight, sound, smell, taste, or touch can throw them into the past, making it difficult to stay in the present.

1.6

Too Much Information And How To Simplify It

As educators, we're acutely aware that forgetting is an impediment to learning. A common battle in our age of too much information and too little time to teach it is the limits of working memory.

Perhaps you have heard of the magical number seven, plus or minus two—maybe in the context of recalling phone numbers.

In 1956, George Miller published what is now a famous paper, "The Magical Number Seven, Plus or Minus Two: Some Limits on Our Capacity for Processing Information,"[1] resolute in the field for being the most cited paper in psychology. In it, Miller proposed that humans can effectively process no more than seven bits, or chunks, of information (plus or minus two) at any given time. This seemed to explain why it was so difficult to remember larger amounts of information at once. In effect, Miller was describing limits of human short-term memory processing, which at that time was still largely a mystery.

This was the initial reasoning behind seven-digit phone numbers. The first three digits (area code) are thought of as a single part, making the entire number within the limits of Miller's Law. Now you may be thinking, "Phone numbers aren't easy to memorize!" Interestingly, soon after Miller published his paper, his colleague—the Nobel Prize–winning economist and educator, Herb Simon—approached him. He advised that while the study had merit, it probably needed to be replicated. Simon estimated that the number seven seemed too high.

Strangely, his observation was largely ignored, and Miller's groundbreaking work was followed by a 40-year hiatus without careful replication. For such important (and famous) work to not be repeated was a scientific anomaly in its own right. The gap in research caused some to ask why a widely cited work on a subject of fundamental and obvious interest had halted rather than inspired further research.

In 2014, Nelson Cowan from the Department of Psychological Sciences at the University of Missouri took up the challenge with help from Miller himself. Cowan used a larger sample and modern methods and did, in fact, replicate the study. His new work reassessed the limits of human working memory. Cowan's research concluded that Simon was right—Miller had overestimated the human capacity for information processing. Consequently, today the generally accepted number is **four plus or minus two**.[2]

Of course, memory is not a constant. The limits of working memory can't be neatly summed up with five little words and tied with a bow. Memory is malleable and adjustable depending on individual focus and training. However, it does follow generalizable rules about **cognitive load**. One way to lessen cognitive load is called chunking.

Chunking is the process of taking a large piece of information and breaking it down into palatable bits of similar content. The most obvious benefit is that a laundry list of ideas becomes just a few categories. The less obvious benefit is that when one of those topics is brought up, it activates a larger neural pathway

in the learner's brain. That's important because the more connections, the greater the power of cognitive processing.

Another benefit of chunking is that it enables an educator to
convey information in a shorter amount of time. Studies show
that the average attention span is incredibly short. According to
the National Center for Biotechnology Information, research
from January 2014 indicates that the average attention span is
8 seconds.[3] In bull riding, that makes money; when presenting
information to an audience, it causes ulcers.

1.7

Prefrontal Cortex: Where We Pay Attention

The **prefrontal cortex (PFC)** is located at the very front of the frontal lobe, just under your forehead. Its frontal position makes intuitive sense because it's the part of your brain responsible for executive function. You can imagine the PFC like the boss over the whole operation of being you. It's your executive director.

The PFC is arguably the most "human" part of your brain, because it separates your cognitive ability from that of other animals. Research shows that primates share PFC functions that are incredibly similar to humans. A recent study looked at the PFCs of 25 volunteers and 25 macaque monkeys (our closest genetic neighbor). While undoubtedly similar, *Homo sapiens* does have one special structure that involves strategic planning, decision making, and cognitive flexibility.[1][2]

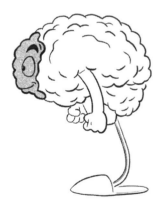

The PFC controls our most advanced cognitive functions, including attention, motivation, planning, problem solving, predicting, articulating, and goal setting. It is the region that enables us to self-manage. The more neuroscientists learn about executive functions, the more we reinforce the term "executive"—they are essential for almost all of the critical decisions we make and all the important outcomes we value.

Humans develop executive function to filter out distractors and temptations that lead to impulsive behaviors. Your prefrontal cortex is what stands between your stomach and that second glass of red wine or calorie-dense dessert. It is what encourages you to compliment Aunt Ida's lipstick or her 1920s hairdo. It is what enables you to have restraint and morality. It allows you to be cool under pressure or to deliver keen insight at precisely the right moment.

Through brain imaging, neuroscientists have found that the prefrontal cortex is the last area of the brain to mature. For most people, it isn't fully developed until somewhere around age 25. Though few of us have the opportunity to witness this phenomenon in the lab, many of us have the opportunity to witness it in our children.

The lengthy development period of the PFC can have tragic consequences. From drug addiction to drunk driving to suicide, the costs can be high for children who are tasked with making adult decisions. Suicide rates in the US are higher than ever before, especially for teenagers. One has to wonder—would the outcome have been different if they'd had fully developed PFCs? It's a sobering reality that we aren't fully developed cognitively until we are well into adulthood, which can sometimes be too late.

Neuroscientists have found a correlation between an early-developed PFC and success later in life. Through a series of studies performed in the late 1960s and early 1970s, Walter Mischel and Ebbe B. Ebbesen found that some children had an easier time with delayed gratification than others.[3] In the famous Stanford marshmallow experiments, children ranging from ages four to six were told they could eat a treat of their choice (a marshmallow, cookie, or pretzel stick) as soon as the researcher left the room. However, if they waited until the researcher came back, they would receive two treats. Waiting for the researcher to return proved difficult for most students. While only a minority of the 600 children tested ate the marshmallow immediately, only about 30% waited long enough to receive a second treat.[4] The researchers found that age greatly impacted whether they could delay gratification.[5]

In follow-up studies, Mischel found a correlation between the results of the marshmallow test and the children's later success.[6] In 1990, Mischel was able to correlate the ability to delay gratification with higher SAT scores.[7] And a later study from a sample of the original Stanford participants showed that the students who had waited for a treat had more brain activity in the PFC when they reached middle age.[8]

Most managers, teachers, instructional designers, and parents do not consider that the PFC could be primed for higher-order executive function. As educators, we have been more reactive than engaged when it comes to understanding how the brain works and how people learn. Therefore, we tended to reward or punish rather than strategize about growing neural circuits and myelinating connections between the various lobes of the brain and the prefrontal cortex.

1.8

Your World's Gatekeeper

The first time I (Kieran) heard the word *amygdala*, I couldn't even spell it. Now I wonder how I survived so long without understanding it. Like many structures in the brain, there are two amygdalae, one in each hemisphere. Each small structure is located above the RAS filter and below the hippocampus. It is most closely associated with the hindbrain but is not inside it.

The **amygdala** is a routing system that decides whether to send information to the forebrain and PFC for executive processing or to send it to the hindbrain. In this way, the amygdala functions as the gatekeeper of a lot of sensory information.

We commonly call the amygdala "Amy" for short. Amy chooses whether to route sensory information into the reactive brain or the forebrain based on its state of hyperactivity. When the amygdala is in a hyperactive state, it is about 80% more likely to send information into your hindbrain; when the amygdala is in a calm state, it is much more likely to send information to your frontal lobe for higher-order processing and executive functions.

I'm named after the Greek word for almond because of my shape!

Stress causes the amygdala to go into a hyperactive state. Stressors include emotions like fear, anxiety, boredom, loneliness, and overexcitement, as well as physical sensations like pain, hunger, and exhaustion. Have you ever noticed how difficult it is to concentrate at work when you're hungry? Or how challenging it is to think rationally when you're tired? Ever try to learn a new skill while being chased by a grizzly bear? It won't (can't) happen.

From an evolutionary standpoint, the amygdala is a critical adaptation. When it senses you are in danger, the amygdala sends you into flight, fight, or freeze mode. When you trip on your shoelace, your amygdala sends that information to your hindbrain, and you react by catching yourself with your arm. Isn't it great that you didn't have to consciously decide whether you wanted to catch yourself? By the time you had that thought, you'd already be face down on the ground!

Similarly, when you are startled by a loud noise, your amygdala routes that noise to your hindbrain and you automatically turn your head to look. When you hear a loud noise, especially if it's in the same room as you are, you can't help but look for

the cause. In a lot of ways, you owe your amygdala a lot of gratitude. It keeps you safe and alert.

We are lucky to live in a time and place where we rarely
have to react to many of the stressors of our ancestors (like
starvation and wild animals). Our survival is no longer primarily dependent on fight, flight, or freeze. We have evolved far
beyond animals like dogs, birds, and zebras—yet we still have
all the same equipment (neurologically speaking) to react like
a zebra on the African plain. (As you may have noticed, most
teenagers act more like zebras than humans.)

What happens when a neurobiologist meets the
world's greatest free solo rock climber? Scientist Jane Joseph placed climber Alex Honnold
in an fMRI scanner. Honnold is known around
the world for his incredible risk taking, with his
most notable and mind-boggling achievement a
free solo (without ropes) ascent of El Capitan, a
3,600-foot-high exposed slab of granite in Yosem-
ite Valley. When Joseph looked at Honnold's
amygdala, she saw no notable activation to stimulus that had the control subject (a rock climber of
similar age) "lighting up like a Christmas tree."[1]
Through intentional practice, it appears that over
time, Honnold learned to bypass me, the amygdala, and to process more information in his PFC.

Today, our survival depends primarily on our executive
function. We thrive in the modern world by being able to learn
new concepts and roles. We find meaning and happiness based
on our ability to engage in healthy relationships, maintain steady
employment, and pay the bills.

While your environment has changed over the last thou-
sand years, your brain has not. Despite relying on your active

brain, you are still powerless over your amygdala. You can't help but go into what psychologists refer to as an "amygdala hijack" every time you encounter a stressor.

The problem is, these stressors are *everywhere*. Fear of not being socially accepted, stress from an unfair boss, or boredom from an unexciting learning environment are just a few of the reasons we are reactive. As much as we want to be thoughtful, predictive, and rational, we are usually in fight, flight, or freeze mode. Stress reduces us to a zebra, reacting to what she just said or what he looks like, and to our own thoughts and feelings about ourselves and our environment. We're constantly responding to stress in our lives, both real and imagined.

Amusingly, your amygdala can put you in embarrassing situations.

Name your all-time favorite musical groups in seven seconds...starting now. If you were in front of a crowd when asked to do so, you might be taken aback—you probably couldn't even think straight. You might just stare off into space and utter, "Uhhh..." That's me running the show.

Your inability to control where your amygdala sends sensory information has repercussions far beyond embarrassing yourself. Because your brain is designed to combat short bouts of stress, like being chased by a wild tiger, it is unequipped to deal with the long-term stress that comes from an unreasonable boss or a chaotic life. Chronic stress has a huge impact on your overall health (even shortening your lifespan)[2] and impacts every part of your life, from your sense of well-being to your

relationships. Within the scope of this book, those consequences bleed over to affect your ability to both teach and learn.

For example, imagine
a corporate trainer who
was so stressed from work
that she left the building
early on Friday, canceled a
dinner date, and lounged
in front of the TV all
night. Still exhausted,
she slept in late Satur-
day morning. After some
chores, she again spent
hours in front of the TV.
She didn't want to waste her weekend, but she was just too
tired to do anything else.

On Sunday morning, she woke up and remembered she
had to go back to work the next day. Immediately, she sank
into a debilitating depression, which, once again, she dealt with
by sinking into the same couch. Monday morning, she was
exhausted and stressed. Yet she was somehow supposed to
inspire passionate new hires.

PART II

Learning

2.1

What Is Learning?

In 2006, a large airplane manufacturer began building aircraft with a composite material that resembles what you see today. The shift in technology from metals to composites was dramatic, and subsequently so was the learning curve for the experts tasked with building the new planes. If the company was going to remain profitable during the transition, their thousands of mechanical engineers needed to essentially relearn their jobs... fast. To help things go smoothly and efficiently, the company enlisted a team of learning scientists.

To better understand each other and the problem, the scientists and the engineers did what humans have done for centuries: they convened a formal meeting to draw up plans and basically establish territory. On one side, there were experts on drag, lift, and thrust and on the other, specialists in cognitive priming, learning, and memory. It was safe to say that there were divergent views on almost everything going on in the room. Progress was slow because neither side had the vocabulary nor the deep understanding of the other.

Despite their different backgrounds, there was one topic that interested everyone: lightning strikes. It had never occurred to the learning scientists that engineers actually plan for, and manage, lightning. It seems that lightning can go down through the plane and escape out the back. Soon they understood one reason the engineers were struggling with the new material. Composites are light and strong, but they lack a fundamental property essential to dealing with lightning strikes: conductivity. After a long, contentious morning where it was obvious to everyone that communication was going to be difficult between the disparate groups, it was time for a coffee break.

With communication and lightning in mind, one of the learning scientists overheard a couple of engineers talking about the overhead compartments in planes.

"We drill holes from one compartment to the next for lightning."

"All the way back?" asked the second engineer.

"Yeah. It has a big impact. Saves a lot."

The learning scientist tentatively walked over to the engineers. "Excuse me…you mean to say lightning flows through the space above our heads, where I store my computer? That's unbelievable!"

The engineers looked at him, waiting for him to explain.

"What happens to my computer if lightning strikes it?" asked the scientist.

"What?" The engineers looked at each other.

"Why would lightning strike your computer?" the second engineer asked.

"Well," the scientist explained, "if you drill holes to allow lightning to pass through the overhead compartments, all the way back to the end of the plane, then it's going to have to pass through my computer, right?"

The first engineer grinned. "We do drill…to *lighten* the plane. Reduce weight. Lighten the load."

There it was—the paradigm shift where learning occurred. One minute, lightning meant electricity, the next it meant weight reduction. Lightning became lightening.

Out of that awkward conversation and especially from the laughter that followed emerged a stronger, more collaborative team. Everyone realized that the words they use are specific to their own expertise and schemata for thinking. Now that they could see one another's blind spots, they formed a team by generating ideas and developing a plan for progress.

A shared learning event, like the one above, can be incredibly powerful for those involved. Cocreating knowledge is productive and efficient and leads to knowledge gains that aren't always possible at the individual level.

Definitions of learning are all over the place, depending on whom you ask. A neurologist, psychologist, professor, and kindergarten teacher will all view learning in a correct yet nuanced way. But one thing is sure: most educators agree that before teaching new subject matter, they must first activate prior knowledge. By doing so, the learner can fuse the new information to the old in order to create a better understanding of the whole. From this viewpoint, learning is a process that results in a change in knowledge or behavior as a result of experience. Learners build knowledge as they explore the world around them, observe and interact with phenomena, converse and engage with others, and make connections between new ideas and prior understanding. To learn something, two or more things that were not previously associated with each other become linked together. "Lightning" becomes "lightening."

Something else occurred that the learning scientist hadn't anticipated, something that came as a direct result of this short interaction. The humor released siloed barriers and protected thinking. Everyone was vulnerable. Engineers and scientists laughed together at the misunderstanding and, in doing so, activated an individual neural circuit that flooded the brains of everyone in the room with dopamine (more on that later). Specialists in one area became mere novices in another. And it was okay.

Finally, people could see the others' point of view. Engineers realized why the learning scientists struggled with the composites. At the same time, they benefited from insights into why they themselves had been struggling with pedagogical constructs that were not very real in their daily lives. It was a matter of patterns, or schemas. The constructs they used, the language they preferred—these conceptual spaces were using neural networks with inbuilt schemas that gave meaning to their world. At the point of understanding, they all enjoyed the realization that each of them saw the world in a very different way.

So what happened in the brains of the engineers and scientists? Their respective auditory senses heard the same word. Yet the neural circuits of the learning scientist lit up and retrieved stored knowledge from the hippocampus and the outer cortex that produced bright flashes and loud peals of thunder. The engineers engaged a very different neural circuit, and envisioned formulaic expressions and drilled holes. Once they all understood the misinterpretation, their neural networks reinterpreted the information, and everyone was able to perceive both meanings…with a little humor and embarrassment.

From a neuroscience perspective, the engineers and scientists learned by activating prior knowledge to make sense of the new information. They experienced conceptual change as a result of making visible the preconceptions that each group shared. They also demonstrated cognitive rehearsal through activating all the lobes through vision, speech, audio, articulation, questioning, imagination, and humor. The more they talked about it, laughed about the mistake, and articulated their change in thinking, the more their circuitry around "lightening" and "lightning" established and myelinated. After REM sleep the following night, the information further consolidated and was ready to be encoded into long-term memory.

The process of activating prior knowledge to build on exist-

REM (rapid eye movement) is a sleep cycle where the brain is hard at work consolidating the day's events, encoding important and extraneous information for retention and understanding. It is characterized by rapid eye movements (which is where the name comes from), dreaming, and lack of body movement.

ing knowledge occurs daily in our lives, yet we rarely notice. To witness it, pay attention to children interacting with a parent. Almost every explanation of anything is followed by one of the W questions: when, what, where, who, and why. Their insatiable quest for answers is a search for something that normalizes the new information so they can fit it to an existing schema or create new combinations with association or assimilation. They are looking for something to bridge understanding, anything to connect one concept to another for the purpose of an aha moment.

As educators, our goal is to maximize the pathways associated with the concept or content we're teaching. That way, the learner can retrieve the information efficiently and effectively the next time they use it. One way to strengthen neural pathways is to present the information in a way that engages multiple areas of the brain. Because the brain processes multiple means of presenting the information simultaneously, this information is encoded as an integrated network. When one node activates, the entire network activates.

For instance, pretend you're teaching a child about fractions.

1. To engage multiple areas in the brain, you could first activate the occipital lobe by displaying the information through a visual model, like a number line and fraction bars.

2. Then you can activate the parietal (small motor skills) and temporal (vocalizing) lobes by asking them how much 1/2 + 1/4 of a cookie is. When they respond, give them the whole cookie!

3. Next, ask the child to teach the concept back to you or someone else. This simple activity will engage the PFC, the occipital lobe, the parietal lobe, and various speech areas.

4. Finally, show the child wrong answers (their own as well as others) to further activate the PFC. In doing so, the child will likely experience a meaningful metacognitive moment that stimulates imagination, prediction, and outcome, therefore building and strengthening a neural network around that concept.

By the way, an educator can create an integrated neural network around a concept in adults too. The content might be more complex, but what happens in the brain is more or less the same.

2.2

Dopamine:
The Intrinsic Shortcut To Learning

As educators, we want learners to understand the content, but we also want them to enjoy the process and feel good about the experience; for the learner to truly understand the content, you can't have one without the other. You can likely remember a boss, professor, teacher, or parent who somehow made even the dullest subjects fascinating. For whatever reason, they could make things like company filing systems, plant physiology, or new computer software into something compelling (or at least not bore you to tears).

Remember the 1980 movie *Fast Times at Ridgemont High*?[1] (If you don't, it's worth a Google search.) In his memorable five-point plan, Mike Damone made any situation "the place to be." Although the purpose of his plan was to attract girls, educators might do well by taking a note from Damone's book and make any situation, location, and happenstance the place to be.

So what is that certain something that makes a classroom such a place?

The short answer is dopamine.

Dopamine is a neurotransmitter that is stored in specific neurons in your brain. There are over 100 different neurotransmitters, with the most well-known being dopamine, serotonin, and acetylcholine. These neurotransmitters allow for much

more complex communication than would be possible with electrical synapses alone.

You may recall that when a neuron fires, it sends an electrical impulse called an action potential down the axon to the terminals, where it will be kicked out into the synaptic cleft looking for receptors in the dendritic arborization of another neuron. Of course, the action potential cannot simply jump across the synapse, or gap, between the two neurons. Instead, the action potential is changed into a neurotransmitter via a complex electrochemical process that diffuses the chemical into the space between the neurons.

Once the neurotransmitter reaches the dendrites of another neuron, the neurotransmitter either weakens or strengthens the action potential. It does this by altering the receiving neuron's membrane permeability, which makes it more or less likely to reach threshold and fire another action potential. If the neurotransmitter makes the membrane more permeable, it fires; if it becomes less permeable, the neurotransmitter does nothing and the signal stops (is inhibited).

Some neurotransmitters, like dopamine and oxytocin, make neural circuitry much more efficient. Through chains of synaptic connections, dopamine can help information travel at speeds of up to 100 meters per second, especially if the axonal links are myelinated. Remember, the more efficient and complex the neural circuitry, the greater the ability for cognitive processing.

> Very often, when the brain is not receiving enough dopamine, the student will engage in activities that make them appear that they are not able to focus their attention. The outcome activities often resemble ADD and/or ADHD. In this case, the brain responds through hyperactive behavior to compensate for its deficit in dopamine's comfort and reward.

Not only does dopamine make circuitry more efficient, it also ensures that learners enjoy the learning process, retain more information, and fully understand the content provided. Furthermore, if you bring dopamine into your presentations, you will experience amazing success gaining and maintaining your audience's attention.

When you gain proficiency in your favorite activities, you experience dopamine. It's that personal feeling of achievement and satisfaction you get when you hit the right note on an instrument or when you stand up on a surfboard for the first time. It is that sense of pride and fulfillment when your child scores in basketball or gets their story published in the school paper. Dopamine enhances feelings of contentment, happiness, personal achievement, and success. It makes you feel so good that your brain can't wait to get more.

For that reason, dopamine has been linked to **intrinsic motivation**,[2] or the drive to engage in a behavior because it is enjoyable. When a learner experiences intrinsic motivation, they *want* to learn. Therefore, if dopamine is built into a course or presentation, there is no need for intimidation, punishment, or fear. Instead, the educator relies on the learner's natural curiosity. This kind of motivation highlights learning for learning's sake.

So how does a savvy educator build dopamine into their course? To do so, you first need to understand that dopamine doesn't always act the way you'd expect it to. For example, in a classic study, researchers showed that dopamine was *not* released after the test subjects had completed an assigned task and were in the process of receiving a reward. Instead, dopamine released much earlier, when learners predicted the reward.[3]

At first glance, the findings of this research might surprise you. Dopamine is tricky. However, it explains some of the stranger elements of human behavior. For example, many people are ignited by the chance of winning at the slot machine (even though we all know the chances of winning are minuscule). Despite the odds, people will gamble away their life savings in Las Vegas because deep in their brain is a sudden increase of dopamine receptors. In other words, the dopamine release experienced in association with anticipating a big win overrides any logical decision-making process that would dictate otherwise.

In the same vein, most of us are happy to spend years being broke and overworked in college. In retrospect, those late nights toiling away become some of our fondest memories. What's more, some people who spend decades of hard work to land a great job, a perfect partner, or a big house discover they feel empty once they arrive at their destination. The old maxims are somewhat true: the chase really is better than the prize, and the journey really is more enjoyable than the destination.

If you're lucky enough to have a dad like Rich's, you know how gambling marketing works. Rich's dad taught him that when you see a sign outside a casino that exclaims "OUR SLOTS HAVE A 98% PAYOUT!" you may be thinking, "Wow, my odds are GREAT!" What that sign really means is "FOR EVERY DOLLAR YOU GIVE US, WE'LL GIVE YOU 98 CENTS."

When it comes to teaching, this means that most learners will experience dopamine *during* the learning event (as opposed to some reward after). Therefore, it is imperative to trigger dopamine during the presentation. A teacher can do this by creating lessons that are challenging but attainable with an element of anticipation relating to something exciting.

One way of boosting dopamine levels is through what we call **Me Here Now**. If you can answer the learner's question, "What's in it for me, here and now?" then you will have their attention. That's because when you present material in a context that is relatable to the learner, not only do their dopamine levels increase, but their amygdala will not be needlessly hyperactivated, and sensory data will automatically arrive at the seat of executive function in their PFC.

Good salespeople do this all the time! If a marketer can appeal to the Me Here Now of the customer, they'll get a sale. If they mess up and throw the customer into their amygdala, they've lost it.

On the other hand, if the learner doesn't relate to the content being presented, chances are they will experience boredom. As we mentioned earlier, boredom is an emotion that can result in an amygdala hijack. Teachers see children in freeze, flight, or fight mode in classrooms every day. If a learner is observing something that's boring or unachievable, or if they feel like there's no end in sight, they can't help but check out. Especially if they already have neural circuitry in place that has a negative connotation with the subject matter. That's why talented teachers, salespeople, facilitators, and managers tend to localize and contextualize new information. This allows learners to process it easily because it is meaningful to them, right there and then.

Salience (also called attentional arousal) is another tool you can use to flood the system with neurotransmitters that assist in maintaining focus and enhancing learning. Salience is the quality of being particularly noticeable or important, and it is imperative for dopamine release. When something stands out from its surroundings as a goal or milestone, then the learner is intuitively invested in it. This is particularly meaningful for manipulating and grappling with new information. Salience provides shortcuts to learning new information, as long as the state of salience and information are carefully paired together.

Gabriele, a talented Sicilian illustrator (who created most of the illustrations in this book), is a case in point. When he moved to Milan, he met "a beautiful Russian girl" whom he wanted to know better. The problem? Their common language was broken English. Suddenly, he was motivated to learn English in a way he had never been before. Now that the salience factor was high, Gabriele became fluent in short order. It wasn't long until the two enjoyed each other's company in their new common language while celebrating over a plate of Pasta Pomodoro. Similarly, **emotional arousal** is highly effective at releasing dopamine. A knowledgeable educator can engage situations where a learner's emotions connect and pair with the new information so that they are emotionally invested in the learning. The media has known this for years! As insensitive as it sounds, the newsroom operates under the known—but not publicly declared—mantra of "If it bleeds, it leads." A tragedy means there is an emotional attachment to a story, and therefore it will engage the audience. The question then becomes "How can we connect this story to every listener within earshot?" Below is an example of how a news team could use emotional arousal to transform a story about a fire into a series of headlines and teasers.

Tonight on Action News, local children are crying in the streets, escaping near-certain death, as their homes are devastated by a silent killer...one that could be in your home right now! We'll show you how to keep your home safe tonight at seven!

Children are crying! It could be in your home right now! You could die! How could you not tune in? As the program unfolds, you find out the "silent killer" was a fire, and although there were at few tears, everybody was safely evacuated. You might be a little underwhelmed, but then they interview a sad mother, a concerned neighbor, the fire chief, and some local expert on fire safety. It's all designed to keep your television on, as you tune in later for more details.

Activating emotional arousal isn't always manipulative. Skilled instructors will have success with methods that have universal appeal. For instance, imagine the impact of showing videos of school children playing with kittens. Aww!

Electronic gaming is an excellent example of how dopamine captivates a learner's attention with Me Here Now, emotional arousal, and salience. It is customary for successful game designers to build in elements that ignite intrinsic motivation and connect rewards with "leveling up," or carefully planned incremental achievements. Video games are exciting and visually pleasing. They keep the player engaged with surprising twists and turns that engage Me Here Now.

While attentively playing, individuals are typically making predictions and decisions just in time to avoid losing a level—all neural activities that are associated with higher-order processing in their prefrontal cortices. They turn left to enter a door, they make a prediction about how that choice will impact their character (if perhaps a zombie is waiting for them in the next room), and then they either get a positive or negative result (they blow the zombie's brains out or get overpowered). Occasionally, dopamine is released when they accomplish a challenge or achieve a new level.

Unlike intrinsic motivation, which engages learners for the sake of the learning itself, extrinsic motivation is driven by external rewards such as praise, money, food, and grades.

Interestingly, evidence points to players abandoning previously "hot" games when play focus is associated with **extrinsic**

motivators, and when levels are either not challenging enough or are too challenging.[4] It appears that the process of trying, failing, trying again, and finally succeeding creates an **addictive feedback loop**.

Savvy educators do the same thing in the classroom, the meeting room, the sales floor, and in one-on-one communications. They present materials that are challenging yet attainable. Once their students comprehend the initial material, they "level up" and present content that is even more difficult. As long as the educator is entertaining and provocative and the new material is relevant, the learner will be engaged. The content must always be within the reach of the learner yet complicated enough to be interesting. The long-term effect is a group of learners who view learning as fun and engaging. With that kind of attitude, no matter how difficult the project is or how advanced the concepts are, the learner is optimistic about their ability to understand and is excited about the process.

2.3

Neuroplasticity:
Change Your Brain

None of the information you've read so far in this book will be useful unless you, the educator, are fully aware of the cognitive potential of a learner's brain.

- Do you see intelligence as something that is fixed? As a genetic gift that you were either born with or without?

- Is it something your eleventh-grade teacher slapped on that book report you spent countless hours on with comments like "Substandard" and "Needs Work"?

- Do you perceive ability and talent like the color of your hair, as in something you can dye purple but will always grow out blonde again?

- Do you believe that you have cognitive limits on your ability? That you can only go so far? Or that a certain group of people can only attain so much?

If you answered yes to any of these questions, it's okay. Our education system tends to ingrain this idea in our brains as soon as we enter the formal school system. The moment you are labeled "smart" or "dumb," "gifted" or "ordinary," you are taught for the rest of your life that you will always be that way. From this point, you may adopt a fixed mindset that tends to reinforce these labels. The incredible news is that your brain is plastic, not stone, and that means your mindset can change. Neuroplasticity doesn't mean that the overall shape of your brain can change. We all have the same general brain shape, and you're pretty much stuck with that. What it does mean is that your neural circuitry *can* and *will* change as the connections are reorganized with new experiences. Think about learning a new skill as an adult, like salsa dancing (assuming you've never been a dancer). It's easy to imagine your new neural circuitry wiring. It plays out like a workout montage in a *Rocky* movie. At first, you're terrible at it. Your steps are unbalanced and awkward, you're easily fatigued. You struggle for weeks, maybe months or even years.

However, if you don't leave the class because you're utterly embarrassed, you'll notice that over time, with careful practice and attention from the instructor, the moves become easier. Eventually, move sequences become fluid. You're not quite a fish in water yet, but you see yourself making monumental gains in your ability. You hardly recognize the dancer you were a year ago. You have experienced your neural connections strengthening, multiplying, and myelinating. You are experiencing neuroplasticity.

Almost five decades ago, Donald Hebb at McGill University sought to understand how neuron functions contributed to psychological processes like learning. In his earlier career, Hebb practiced as a classroom teacher who learned firsthand the dangers of extrinsic motivation and behaviorist reward-and-punishment classroom management techniques. Having studied animal behavior at the Yerkes National Primate Research Center, he was eager to abandon stimulus-response principles for understanding learning theory for a more holistic social-emotional stance with regard to human behavior. The result of his research was the theoretical framework capturing plastic phenomena, which he famously summed up as "Neurons that fire together wire together."

To arrive at this conclusion, Hebb examined what he referred to as maze-smart rats and maze-dull rats. Evidence that the healthy mature animal brain is capable of structural plasticity can be traced to his enriched environment studies. These were, in turn, based on findings of enhanced problem-solving behavior in rats living in a complex environment.[1] Rats that lived for weeks in an environment filled with toys that were changed daily in a larger and more complex living space showed increased thickness of cerebral cortical areas. This was also true of aging rats.

Subsequent studies found that cortical neurons showed increased dendritic branching and complexity in enriched environments compared with normal laboratory cages.[2] Furthermore, we've found that not only can intelligence increase, it can decrease as well. Neuroscientists have observed neuronal degradation due to stressors that caused dendritic arborization to be curtailed and pruned. Chronic stress is one such factor that causes neurons to shrink but not necessarily to die.[3]

Based on further lesion studies, researchers examined the reorganization of cortical maps in various areas in adult human brains and discovered incontrovertible evidence that neural systems are modifiable networks.[4]

Today, we know that plasticity is real. And, although there is evidence that supports the view that the younger the animal or child, the more malleable the neuronal circuitry, neuroscientists verified that malleable neural circuitry and related processes are not limited to "sensitive" periods or "windows of opportunity" in early childhood development.[5] Modern neuroscience adopts the idea of a *permanently* plastic brain. This has widespread and meaningful implications for all of us—your intelligence is not fixed!

2.4

Every Thought Counts

The realization that plasticity is a thing and that "neurons that fire together wire together" changed the way educators viewed learning and intelligence. Typically, by activating prior knowledge, a learner can make meaning out of new information with a process that involves conceptual change.[1]

At the neural level, a permanently plastic brain looks very basic: it's your brain's capacity to rewire and reorganize itself at will.[2]

When you learn something, millions of dendritic spines literally grow to form complex electrochemical circuits that involve axons and receptor terminals of new neurons. Neuroplasticity is almost like using GPS to get from one place to another. When you miss a turn, the GPS reroutes to get you to your destination. You learn that there's more than one way to get there, and that knowledge delivers a bigger world view on how to travel from one place to another.

What's more, the old saying "Use it or lose it" is also true. Pathways that have gone out of use will be pruned away but can be reactivated. Although it will take a bit of time to put these circuits into practice again.

In the same vein, conventional wisdom used to predict that practice makes perfect. A judicious element of neuroscience will confirm that this is essentially a myth. In fact, practice makes permanent. Without mediation from coaches, mentors, and teachers, years of incorrect practice will never deliver the expected results. Rich's coach, world champion team roper Mike Beers, got it right when he said, "Practice makes perfect if you practice perfect." With Mike's help, Rich can rope.

The adage is true in the classroom or the workplace. To engage meaningful neural pathways, the educator's job is to mediate each learner's practice, thinking, or attitude. As an instructor, training supervisor, teacher, or parent, intentionality in relation to cognitive rehearsal will mean all the difference between a learner experiencing cognitive overload or that same student learning with deep understanding.

Changing one's diet is a perfect example of intentional practice. Let's say you want to lose a few pounds and feel a little healthier. Every method you've tried in the past has failed. Then you read, for example, *The Plant Paradox* by Dr. Steven Gundry, and you find out that lectins are your personal nemesis.[3] So you cut out nightshades and limit animal protein, and your paradigm changes. Suddenly it's what you *don't* eat that becomes important.

At first, your brain persistently reminds you that you like certain foods that aren't healthy for you. But over time, you actively change that circuit. Six weeks later, your neural circuits are different in relation to your eating habits. You accept easily that a plate of roasted veggies for breakfast sounds just right, and your scale reflects a loss of 22 pounds. You changed your brain as well as the way you think about and consume food.

In *The Talent Code*, author Daniel Coyle suggests that intentional practice can cram six months of learning into about six minutes.[4] Of course, there is no way to know the exact numbers for sure, but what we can say with certainty is that intentional practice makes the learner *dramatically* more efficient.

Intentional practice doesn't need to be completely prescriptive either. Remember how engaging all sensory inputs with the different cerebral lobes creates a larger neural network? By facilitating the use of multiple sensory protocols (like sight, hearing, touch, and smell), an educator can help the learner generate a mental model about how their brain engages with the new information so that stronger, more complex neural connections are created. These sensory activators can involve just about anything, like reading, looking at graphics and charts, listening to a podcast, or discussing the content with someone else.

You may have already realized that this kind of practice not only creates more complex neural connections, it also facilitates strengthening of myelin structures. More connections and attention means that the learner will increase their capacity to perform better and process information faster.

This kind of practice not only applies to motor skills; it also applies to our thoughts. You not only are what you eat—you are what you think! Realizing that the more we practice something, the stronger our neural circuits become shows us that there is literally an electrochemical corollary to what we think and what we do.

Essentially, when you are happy, the sensation occurs because a bunch of neurons in your brain are managing the happy feeling or thought. When you're sad, it is just the same. The more time you spend associating a positive feeling with a certain action, the less likely you associate a negative feeling with that action. The more often you perform an activity, have a thought, or experience a feeling, the stronger the connection and the more efficient you become at processing that data. In other words, we are all responsible for our feelings, thoughts, and reactions to life.

There is value in perceiving brains as circuitry. All thoughts, feelings, and emotions are determined by electrical signals in the brain, and once we realize that everyone's brain is malleable and its circuitry can be rewired, it is easy to understand our role in reorganizing those pathways. Educators can help learners (and themselves) change any circuit of neurons that are preventing them from reaching their full potential.

Anyone can learn and do anything. Capacity is endless. Potential is limitless. We all have brains with wiring that is ever-changeable.

It's true what they say—it's all in the mind. The notion of cocreating our neural circuits in the pursuit of life is powerful and important. It means the real secret to becoming the person we want to be lies in what we think, our mental models. In realizing our own agency over our thoughts, it's clear that we are not victims of a poor neural happenstance; we are in fact in full control of our faculties. That's why every thought counts.

Agency is a social cognition theory perspective in which people are producers as well as products of social systems.

2.5

Pulling It All Together: Neuroscience, Growth Mindset, And You

If a learner thinks they aren't going to be able to learn something, guess what? Their brain facilitates a group of neurons that immediately build a neural circuit to confirm that very belief. Their RAS will filter information into their PFC to confirm it. The more stressed they become over the content, the more information they will send to their amygdala, and the less information they will retain. A neural circuit will strengthen and myelinate around the negative loop, and the learner will create a self-fulfilling prophecy.

Of course, it isn't all doom and gloom. On the contrary, those who realize the same is true of positive beliefs can construct a much more powerful brain and a richer life in every respect.[1] This is the key to the door of learning.

On September 1, 2014, Rich and his daughter, AnneMarie, drove off to a rodeo event. On this beautiful morning, with the sun shining and time on their hands, they hopped aboard his Harley-Davidson and decided on a leisurely drive through the backroad foothills of Mount Rainier. Here is Rich's account of the power we all have over our own brains.

We were less than 15 minutes from our house when a driver on an intersecting street ran through a stop sign at 45 miles per hour. Broadsided, we flew across the street and landed…hard…in a ditch. The Harley was totaled, but in retrospect, it fared better than we did.

My son, Jesse, arrived on the scene. He called for medical assistance as several bystanders ran over to help.

AnneMarie had a severe concussion, a shattered shin, and a broken hip. Somehow, she remained conscious the entire time and was taken to a nearby hospital.

I didn't do as well. Later, we'd joke that I acted as AnneMarie's "air bag." Doctors told me I took the full force of the collision. Apparently, I had stiff-armed the oncoming vehicle, and in the process sandwiched my right leg between both vehicles. It bore the brunt of 4,000 pounds impacting at 45 miles per hour.

I suffered a full right-arm avulsion (separation) and my right leg was crushed below the knee. Oh, and my femur had exploded through my hip. Most of the bones on my right side were broken or displaced.

On the seventeenth day in ICU, they started to reassemble me. My arm was reattached, and my leg was amputated below the knee.

When I awakened, through the haze of medication, I asked, "How is AnneMarie?"

I was so relieved that she was recovering nicely in another hospital an hour away. My brother, Jake, visited every morning with updates on her condition as well as some jasmine tea (at my request) and ginger root candies.

I was in surprisingly good spirits. I was just happy that my daughter and I were alive. With my left hand, I made daily journal entries in my laptop. I wrote down thoughts, stories, and random entries. When I wasn't writing, I spent endless hours researching "how to walk again" with a prosthetic I had yet to be fitted for—and without even knowing whether I would be able to walk again.

Rather than telling myself I was handicapped, I read science journals on the subject, watched endless videos, continued to journal, and visualized myself doing everything I could do before the accident. I relentlessly questioned surgeons, nurses, and hospital staff on any secrets they might have to achieving my goal.

My conclusion? "It's all in my head."

Today, Rich is a sought-after speaker and educator on this very subject and a first-person example of the brain's amazing powers. To see him or speak to him casually, you would never imagine what his body went through or what his thoughts, exercises, and neuroplasticity delivered in short order.

Every brain is equipped with about the same number of neurons as every other human brain. Each of these brains has the ability to create new and better circuitry. Intelligence is malleable; brainpower is grown. Learners are limited by their own beliefs, not their innate abilities.

And if understanding the human brain's potential is the key to the door of learning, as an educator, you have influence in opening (or closing) that door. Those who don't understand that every healthy brain has limitless capability are part of the problem. No matter the classroom, they have a responsibility to their learners not to reinforce circuitry that further traps them in a negative mindset. Instead, they should empower the learner to take charge of their experience. When learners actively change the filters, when they lay down new neural circuitry, everything changes. Surprising opportunities show up, remarkable possibilities appear, and huge intellectual gains are made.

Your job boils down to one question: How can I facilitate a learning space that works with these new mental models?

As an educator, you are uniquely positioned to shape the mind of the learner. Researcher Aneeta Rattan and her colleagues asked math teachers to describe what they would say to encourage a student who had failed their first math test of the year. They found that the adults in a **fixed mindset** would usually say something like, "It's okay, not everyone is good at math." Teachers using a **growth mindset** approach would respond, "Try harder!" and then give the student practical advice so they could do better in the future.[2]

Imagine what might happen if we went beyond that model and focused only on the questions that the student got right instead of what they got wrong? If we stopped labeling and stratifying based on snapshots of proficiency?

Data from the Kahn Academy experiment indicate that all children can earn an A.[3] Some do it immediately, some take a little time, and others take a little more time. But we do not punish them based on the snapshot of a particular day. Many studies have shown that students who entered the classroom as low achievers and were taught by an instructor with a fixed mindset ended up showing little improvement throughout the year.[4] This is referred to as the **Pygmalion Effect**, and it basically confirms what the teacher believes the child will achieve, as if in a self-fulfilling prophecy.[5][6] (Remember RAS?) In contrast, low-achieving students educated by an instructor with a growth mindset showed progress.

It is critical that we reinforce positive beliefs in ourselves and in others. Show the learner that their brain is malleable. Help them understand that their potential is limitless. Once they believe this, they will do the work for you. We have found that when educators adjust their own thinking about how the brain works, the learning space changes. It becomes more inviting, more engaging, easier to achieve, and more fulfilling to succeed in.[7]

By educating people on how the brain processes new information most effectively, we can create a healthier and more adjusted workforce; better teachers, presenters, facilitators, and sellers; and more knowledgeable parents. When we truly understand how stress impacts neural capacity, we must surely adopt attitudes, methods, and practices that will not only alleviate stress but will also engage us in productive challenges that make stress more accessible and ultimately make life more palatable.

*   *   *

BRAIN BREAK: SENTENCE-BY-SENTENCE STORY

This brain break explores the idea of creativity and works well for any group of people. (You might want to remind those participating to be mindful of cultural and personal sensitivities as well as implicit bias.) All you need is a piece of paper and a pen. Start by writing a sentence. It can be about anything! Then ask other people to write another sentence that continues the story. You can leave it in the break room or wherever your team gathers informally. By the end of the day, you'll have a hilarious story that everyone contributed to. This brain break is great for unleashing creativity by prompting the participants to think predictively and to use humor.[8]

PART III

Behaviorism

3.1

You Get An "A" And You Get An "F"

Like most of us, you struggle against an outdated model of teaching. We're not just talking about in the classroom either. You fight this process every time you train a new hire, every time you learn a skill yourself, and every time you teach your child something new. You're not alone—almost everyone uses this technique to some degree, more often subconsciously than consciously.

It's not your fault either. You're just using the tool you're most familiar with. You were introduced to this method in grade school, immersed in it by high school, inundated with it through higher education. And by the time you entered the workforce, it had solidified into your psyche. It's likely the only approach to teaching you've ever had any real experience with, so why would you think to use anything else?

This model of teaching is derived from the behaviorist school of thought. It shows up variously as operant conditioning, instrumental learning, stimulus-response, and classical conditioning. We often refer to it as a reward-punishment method because no other name calls it exactly what it is. Behaviorism operates in a system where rewards for good behavior are intended to increase that action, while punishment for bad behavior is designed to decrease that action.[1] It's an intuitive, simple idea. And according to a lot of people, it works. At least it does some of the time…sort of.

We've found that it works great for dogs, cats, and pigeons—at least for *hungry* dogs, cats, and pigeons—but it doesn't work for people…especially people who aren't hungry.

Right from the beginning, many scientists in fields that studied animal behavior, psychology, and education expressed reservations about the efficacy of behaviorism as a teaching method and objected to many of the dogmas that were associated with it. For instance, Donald Hebb as early as 1937 had grave misgivings about Pavlovian behaviorism (involving stimulus-response) as a basis for understanding psychological phenomena as they related to learning.[2] In his book *The Organization of Behavior*, he outlined an entirely new way of understanding behavior in terms of brain function.[3] From his vantage point at the Yerkes Primate Research Laboratory, he was able to distinguish variations in animal intelligence between large-brain species (primates) over work that was carried out on smaller brains (rats and pigeons) and thus moved away from the constraints of external thinking and stimulus-response learning models. His work revolutionized psychology by establishing a biological basis for psychological phenomena. He delivered a neuropsychological theory that provided the structure for the development of the fields of cognitive and behavioral neuroscience.

Despite Hebb's groundbreaking work in revolutionizing the theoretical underpinnings of learning, it appears that mainstream teaching practice became entrenched in behaviorist methodologies. In this next section, we will explore what behaviorism was and is today and how it impacts your learning system.

Based on Pavlov's famous conditioning experiments and later work by Watson, Thorndike, and Skinner, behavioral psychologists formalized this new science of psychology: **behaviorism**. Skinner in particular brought behaviorism to education. He hypothesized that people were born with a *tabula rasa*, Latin for "clean slate." He argued that children had metaphorically empty heads that were ready to be filled by everything they experienced throughout their lives. Based on that notion, philosophers and behavioral psychologists alike argued that free will is an illusion, making human action the mere result of consequences from previous efforts.[4] From this point of view, educators (and all life experiences) were the builders and children were the materials.

In practice, behaviorism operates on opposing ends of a continuum that resolves consequences for actions. It looks like this: the strength of a behavior is modified by either a reward (which increases the strength) or punishment (which decreases the strength).[5] On both sides of the divide (rewards and punishments), there are positive and negative overlays based on the presence or absence of a stimulus.

For instance, with **reinforcement,** to increase the desired behavior, it is easy to associate a positive stimulus (treat) with your dog obeying your command (or a child getting an A for being compliant). At the same time, a noxious stimulus can be removed to achieve the same behavior. This might look like a person hitting the snooze button on their alarm clock (to escape from the crisis) or a child studying hard so that they can avoid getting a bad grade or upsetting their dad (active avoidance).

Similarly, on the **punishment** side of the equation, to decrease the unwanted behavior, there are activities associated with adding a noxious stimulus (such as beating or berating a child) and avoiding the noxious stimulus (such as being sent to the principal's office or sent to their room).

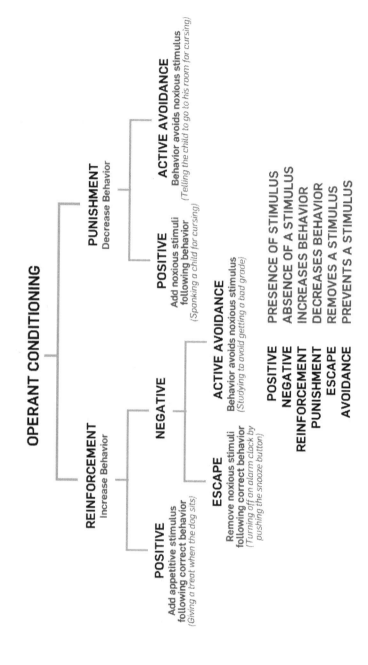

If you've ever trained a pet, you've put behaviorism into practice. Let's say you want Rich's dog, Buda, to sit. To use **positive reinforcement**, you grab a couple of pieces of bacon (reinforcing behavior by adding a stimulus) and hold them over Buda's head. If he sits, he gobbles down bacon while you say the word "sit" (a neutral stimulant, like Pavlov's metronome). If Buda doesn't sit, you use **negative reinforcement** by disengaging and ending the game (reinforcing behavior by taking away a stimulus). If Buda wants to continue the game to avoid being bored or lonesome, he might sit to get your attention. How often have you seen a dog perform every trick it knows, frantically sitting, rolling over, and shaking, desperately hoping the game will continue?

Now let's say that Buda loathes the mailperson. Every time the postal van drives by, Buda barks like crazy while zooming around the furniture. Annoyed, you try something new. When Buda barks, you tell him to get in his kennel or a back room of the house, removing the stimulus from him in the hopes that will keep him from barking in the future (punishing behavior by taking away a stimulus). The last tool in the behaviorist tool box is **positive punishment**. Examples of positive punishment for dogs include bark collars designed to administer electric shocks when the dog barks and choke collars (punishing behavior by adding a stimulus).

Most animal lovers and modern trainers avoid positive punishment. In practice, old-school animal trainers love to market positive punishment as "conditioned response training," as a euphemism that includes painful methods like whipping and hitting.

As we've mentioned, behaviorism isn't just practiced on animals. In fact, it is the most common method of teaching in classrooms, whether your classroom is a training room, boardroom, sales room, or your kid's bedroom). When a teacher (Ms. Maple) conditions a child (James) to get good grades using positive reinforcement, she rewards him with something he desires, like a cookie or an A. When Ms. Maple conditions her student James using negative reinforcement, he is motivated to achieve a certain grade to avoid something unpleasant. For example, he might stay up studying the night before a test to avoid a bad grade. As James grows older, he may decide not to pursue a certain subject matter so that he can escape the potential F and the subsequent social ramification for being labeled "dumb." If Ms. Maple uses negative punishment, she might send James to a different room for acting out in class. In this scenario, the teacher punishes the child by removing him from the classroom in the hopes of decreasing the behavior in the future.

Fifty years ago, positive punishment usually took the form of a beating, like a teacher spanking a child for acting out. Today, positive punishment is generally in the form of an emotional or mental berating, like intentionally embarrassing the child in front of the class, detaining them after school, forcing them to miss recess, or having them write a letter to the principal. Although more difficult to spot, today's version of positive punishment is just as painful as it was five decades ago.

3.2

Behaviorism Is Outdated

You may be thinking, *Of course I use the behaviorist method! It works, doesn't it?* Many people believe that the behaviorist method is the best way—the only way—to get their employees, students, and children to do what they expect them to. On an intellectual level, it makes sense that an employee who is compliant with the company culture and completes assignments on time deserves a raise, promotion, or better office space. It also makes sense that an employee who fails to do so may be passed up for a promotion, moved to another department, or even fired.

Similarly, a child might be rewarded with an allowance or a snack if they finish their chores. If they fail to do so, they will not receive their reward and might even be grounded or have a toy taken away. We'll agree that the behaviorist method does work in some situations. For example, a child won't touch a hot stove more than once. We learn quickly from pain.

We bet you can see yourself in this scenario. In preschool, depending on the teacher and the classroom environment, you were somewhat free to experiment as you learned. No one was grading you on your Lego house or your finger paintings. What's more, you weren't wondering whether your Lego houses were good or bad. Instead, you were simply delighted by the act of creating something out of nothing. You were more or less able to learn how to interact with other children and the world around you on your own terms, in your own way.

Once you entered kindergarten, however, things changed. You received your first grades, cleverly disguised as star stickers or smiley faces. At this young age, the education system already stratified you as a three-star, two-star, one-star, or no-star student. You could barely tie your shoes, yet you could already separate the "smart" kids from the "dumb" kids. You then grew into grade school, aptly named for the time in your life that arbitrary letters A–F dictated your self-worth. At six years old, you could clearly see some of your classmates advancing more quickly than others.

As you moved through the grades, this structure became more and more apparent. By high school, some children and young adults received college credit, while others struggled in remedial classes. If you graduated from high school, you decided whether to continue your education or join the workforce. Your high school GPA greatly influenced that decision. Whatever route you chose, this system further stratified you.

If you went on to college, you continued as an A–F student, with your average letter grade determining whether you could advance to postgraduate education, and subsequently determining how much money you would make as an adult.

If you pursued employment, that A turned into a raise, a better office space, or prestige among your colleagues. That F transformed into poor work reports or downward movements in the company.

What happened to the brain with limitless potential? Had it not been present in first grade and all the way up through university? Why did stratification and labeling prevent some students from achieving their true potential? Do you know people who fell by the wayside in this perverse academic and stratified journey? When it gets personal, we see traction. When it is "my child" or "my sister or brother" who is struggling in a reward–punishment system, then we are willing to look deeper into the situation and suggest solutions that make sense from a neuro-biological standpoint.

In his book *The Orchid and the Dandelion*, Dr. Boyce describes a devastating situation that occurred in his middle-class family where his sister, whose autonomic nervous system indicated her sensitivity to labeling and stratification in social context, caused her life outcomes to be diametrically opposite to his own life trajectory.[1]

Boyce uses the terms "orchid" and "dandelion" to describe two different types of learners. Dandelions, despite being raised in a behaviorist model, persevere and thrive anyway (kind of like the ubiquitous yellow weed). Orchids, like the temperamental-yet-beautiful plant, need the exact right conditions in order to thrive (think greenhouse).

We all know people like this in our families, workplaces, and schools. Such "orchid" souls fare poorly in a reward–punishment system that pushes people out rather than inviting them in. Incidentally, the remainder of people—whose sensitivity in their **autonomic nervous system** (the part controlling subconscious bodily functions) is more closely associated with resilience and grit—don't do any better in a structure that allows them to slide by with the barest minimum, as they easily learn to "game" the system.

The K–12 system is a prime example of a reward–punishment model that does not work. Every year in the United States, over 1.2 million students drop out of high school. That's 1 student every 26 seconds, or 7,000 students a day.[2] Furthermore, the US, which historically had some of the highest graduation rates of any developed country, now lags behind.[3] In 2017, Finland had a high school graduation rate of 99% and Japan had a rate of 98%. At the same time, America fell far below New Zealand, South Korea, the Netherlands, Canada, China, and Germany, with a rate of 83%.[4] In addition, 32 million adults in the United States can't read, according to the U.S. Department of Education and the National Institute of Literacy.[5] Clearly, children in the behaviorist system find it difficult to reach their potential.

Learning scientists often witness this firsthand. The following account is of a school visit from a scholar who helps teachers shift from behaviorist methods to neurocognitive methods.

As a learning scientist, I spend a lot of time in schools across the US. I offer support to teachers and staff who are working to include a more neuro-informed method. When I arrive, I am usually asked to wait in the main office or a corridor. Here it is impossible not to observe punitive behaviorist remedies applied to children by people who believe they are acting in their best interest.

One day, while seated in the main office to await my meeting with the principal, a young girl walked through the door. She was a little overweight and looked to be about 10 years old. I watched her shuffle over to the front desk, head down and obviously uncomfortable.

"I'm finished," she announced sheepishly as she placed a math worksheet on the front desk.

"Good girl!" an office worker responded. The worker then reached over to a glass jar filled with M&M's. She opened the jar, pulled out a single piece of candy, and placed it in the child's chubby palm. "You can go back to your class now."

Without so much as a grin or even the slightest bit of eye contact, the girl sidled out of the room, popped the M&M into her mouth, and returned to her classroom.

Apparently, she had been taken out of class because she was unable to complete her math assignment. She was then isolated and placed in a room by herself until she completed a worksheet that presumably she didn't understand in the first place. When she finished, she was instructed to go to the office for her "reward." They praised her in the same way you'd praise a puppy. *Good girl!*

This child learned a lot from that experience. Her RAS, amygdala, and hippocampus were busy processing new information (or consolidating old beliefs) that would remain with her for life. She learned that she wasn't as smart as the other kids. She learned that if she didn't understand something, she shouldn't ask questions. Otherwise, she'd be embarrassed and isolated. She learned not to trust teachers and adults. She learned that school is a place she didn't like, and a place that didn't like her back. She learned that food was a reward and stratification was a punishment, and that teachers, office workers, and principals were the enemy.

What she didn't learn, unfortunately, was math. She didn't learn that her brain is plastic and that knowledge is grown, not inherited. She didn't learn that she has the same potential as every other student, and she didn't leave that office convinced her brain is every bit as brilliant as everyone else's. She didn't learn that she has the capacity to achieve whatever she puts her mind to. She learned that she is limited, not limitless.

Sadly, her experience is common. In fact, Rich's son, Jesse, had a similar experience in school.

> Despite his potential, Jesse wasn't as excited about learning at school as when he learned things on his own. The final straw for me was when I was called into a parent-teacher conference and the teacher asked, "Now which one is Jesse?"
>
> This educator didn't even know who my son was, yet had the audacity to claim he was the problem. I pulled him and my daughter out of school right afterward and we began homeschooling. We would read about it, work on it, try it out on the farm, look it up on YouTube. Both kids excelled with this educational approach as they segued to additional schooling, college, and work life.
>
> At 19, Jesse now makes an amazing living. He recently bought a five-acre farm, has a new car, keeps a flexible budget, understands collaboration and cocreation in the workspace, and is on the fast track. He's a critical thinker who now teaches others his trade and is enjoying life to its fullest.

The behaviorist system delivers rewards that do not work and punishments that build defense mechanisms that keep children at a plateau of below-average ability. When these students enter the workforce, they carry the problems of the K–12 system with them. Trends (according to the Bureau of Labor Statistics) show that more jobs now require postsecondary education, and that trend is predicted to increase.[6] Yet schools remain in a system where they fail to produce confident, well-rounded critical thinkers. It's no wonder so many corporate leaders decry the prospect of hiring new graduates, because they are so unsuited for the workplace.[7][8]

Furthermore, businesses often operate in the same reward–punishment schema that schools do, and subsequently produce stress, anxiety, and fear that manifests in unhealthy habits so employees fail to reach their potential.

Aside from the devastating moral, ethical, and social costs of traditional teaching methods, behaviorism is also responsible for huge corporate monetary losses. Researchers attribute those losses to poor employee engagement, low workplace satisfaction, attrition, and silly errors. Ask any Human Resource director the expense of attrition, which includes the cost of training and then losing that employee, as well as hiring another who then enters that same costly cycle. It's a devastating bottom-line dilemma.

3.3

What Your Boss Is Doing Wrong

Most corporate training courses are solidly entrenched in the behaviorist methodology. Some variants have arisen in industry in an effort to keep up with technological advances, and they typically fall into the categories of compliant, prescriptive, and systematic. For all the cost, technological wizardry and hype, they are still behaviorist in outlook and planning and only delay inevitable behaviorist outcomes that we already detailed with regard to extrinsic motivation, external rewards and punishments and stimulus–response encounters. For instance, the five phases of instructional design abbreviated as ADDIE (analysis, design, development, implementation, and evaluation)[1] or the terminal objectives of a Dick and Carey model[2] comply closely with reward-and-punishment prescriptive methodologies and deliver exactly that.

In practice, these models (and others like them) generally manifest as a single presenter, or owner of the information, talking for hours in front of an incredibly dull presentation filled with knowledge that is often completely inaccessible to the learner due to cognitive overload. In the process, the presenter is obligated to "cover" all of their terminal objectives, or a list of 50+ items that management has deemed important for compliance. Bonus points if the presenter covers every topic before lunch. So much information in so little time.

At the end of the demonstration, the presenter might say something like, "Does anyone have any questions?" or "What have we learned today?" to an audience who hasn't processed anything in their PFC since the first five minutes of the presentation (and subsequently are falling asleep in their chairs).

Behaviorists regard this as a time for the audience to clarify any issues that might have emerged during the fire hose of information. Cognitivists humorously refer to this as the "Anyone, anyone?" syndrome, referring to the movie *Ferris Bueller's Day Off,* where Ben Stein plays the monotonous and expressionless economics teacher.[3]

In 2008, one of our colleagues was hired by a large manufacturer to help instructional designers devise material for employees who needed to switch from a traditional manufacturing process to a modern one based on the discovery of new techniques and material innovations. In the process, he gained a firsthand account of how inefficiently some of the biggest companies in the world train their employees. Here's a quick description of one of the expensive classes he was invited to observe while assessing the situation for next steps.

> To understand where my team and I were needed, we attended one of the company's training seminars. We sat down with the engineers and gazed up at the large screen displaying a slide presentation. After reading the first slide, we exchanged a look that unmistakably said, "Oh no." The acronym projected on the screen, presumably intended to facilitate learning, was WYFTCYWK.* There weren't even any vowels!
>
> The instructor said, "After you finish this course, you'll know what this acronym means." I couldn't believe that this was his big idea for the class! The

only thing I remember about that course was the acronym, and I remember it as a perfect example of what *not* to do. While he was speaking, I looked around the room. Half the engineers were asleep, while the other half were bored to tears.

Afterward, we asked the attendees what they remembered from the meeting. The most common response was, "Those seats were really uncomfortable!" Based on the first slide, we weren't surprised that the engineers didn't remember anything about the innovative materials design that had ironically been the central topic for the course.

*WYFTCYWK stood for "When you finish this class, you will know.[4]

It turns out that this kind of training proves incredibly expensive for industry. Moving out of the traditional behaviorist model alone would save corporate America millions of dollars daily by helping them train new employees right the first time and getting them up to speed more quickly. Imagine a class where when the workers exited, they were still asking really important questions like, "What do you think would happen if we did this instead…" or "I love the idea of [concept], but why don't we try to look at what [other company] tried to do instead?"

When employees end up spontaneously generating questions, coming up with new ideas and feeling that their ideas are important, accepted, and welcomed, the corporate culture changes and the employee contribution experiences a multiplicative effect.[5]

3.4

Why Incentives Don't Work

Reliance on extrinsic motivation to convey knowledge is one of the most glaring issues with traditional teaching methods. **Extrinsic motivation**, which is derived from external factors, is problematic because it isn't the *right* motivator for the brain. It's clear that using an M&M to motivate an overweight child to do her math homework is wrong. You might even argue that it is unethical. Of course, not all extrinsic motivations are immoral. For example, common workplace incentives include raises, bonuses, better office space, and more control. Yet these incentives often don't elicit the response management hoped for. At least, not in the long term.

Author Alfie Kohn argues that reward and punishment-based systems fail to produce long-term results. He calls this phenomenon "temporary compliance," meaning extrinsic motivators only work for simple tasks over a short duration.[1] Have you ever failed to keep up with a new exercise plan or diet? You were likely suffering from **temporary compliance**, in that the reward of losing weight was only captivating enough to get you to perform for a short period of time. Unless you found an intrinsic motivator, you likely slid back into your old routine.

The simplest neurological explanation for temporary compliance is **homeostasis**. The brain is always trying to bring us into this state of stability. This means your brain will compensate for unusual stimuli. If you regularly consume caffeine, homeostasis is essentially the reason you feel lethargic before you have your morning cup of coffee or tea. Because your brain knows it receives coffee every morning at seven o'clock, a group of neurons team up and release chemicals to make you sleepy in anticipation. If you drink your usual dose, you'll end up feeling relatively normal. If you don't get any caffeine, you'll be groggy (and possibly have a headache). If you drink an extra cup, you'll feel awake and jittery.

What's interesting is that the stimulus doesn't have to be a chemical like caffeine to produce a response in your brain. Consider addictive behavior like using a cell phone or playing a computer game. If you use a phone to feel relaxed, your brain will activate neuro-pathways that make you feel tense in anticipation. If you can't use your phone, you'll end up feeling anxious. Doesn't it drive you crazy when your phone dings or lights up and you're unable to answer? If it doesn't bother you, think about what it does to a teenager.

Research shows pervasive "phantom vibrations" in teens. This pheromone phenomenon is a tactile hallucination caused by your brain perceiving a sensation that is not actually there. Phantom vibrations haunt approximately 9 out of 10 teenagers. They report the sensation while taking a shower, watching TV, or simply walking the dog. Listen...I think your phone is calling you right now![2]

Your brain has an incredible ability to reorganize itself around new experiences, enabling you to quickly adapt to both positive and negative events. Homeostasis can be a subtle and adversarial foe. Your brain's desire to stabilize also occurs in the workspace. Imagine an employee who has just received a major promotion. On their first day, they have a sensory overload. Everything is new and luxurious. Their new office is spacious, with large windows and a view. Their desk looks expensive, and their new chair is so comfortable. Everyone even treats them differently...*better*. But after a few years, they normalize the promotion. What used to be extraordinary is ordinary. Yet the only change that took place since the promotion was the one in their brain. Not unlike someone getting hooked on a drug (from a neurological standpoint), the only way they can score another high is by receiving another promotion. As far as your brain is concerned, extrinsic motivation is a drug. It will make you feel good for a while, but you can never get enough of it.

Another issue with behaviorism is that it is fear-based. In the best-case scenario, a learner is afraid of not receiving positive reinforcement. In the worst-case scenario, the learner is afraid of receiving punishment. Both of these situations are stressful and therefore raise cortisol levels. Cortisol activates your amygdala, routing sensory data to your hindbrain. Instead of processing information in your PFC, you're in flight, fight, or freeze mode. You can't help it—it's an automatic response to fear.

Cortisol is a hormone produced by the adrenal glands. It helps your body respond to stress and the fight, flight, or freeze response associated with me!

Furthermore—unless you receive positive reinforcement—in the behaviorist system, your RAS filter is likely set to filter out the positives. Remember how your RAS acts as an information filter based on what you deem as important or necessary for survival? It's the reason you can suddenly hear your name when it's called in a crowded room.

Let's say that Adam loves his job, but for one reason or another he's been late for a week straight. His manager calls him into her office and says something like, "You've been late five times this week. I'm going to dock that time from your pay." While you might argue that Adam deserves to be punished, that punishment recalibrates his RAS filter. Now he is more likely to process cues from the environment that reinforce the idea that he is constantly tardy. As we mentioned before, this can become a self-fulfilling prophecy, so the thought "I am rarely late," transitions to "I am usually late."

What's more, the behaviorist method of teaching generally relies on rote memorization. This schema is the traditional method of teaching where the main idea is bullet-pointed out and the educator crams all the info into the learners' minds. Hence the phrase "cramming for a test."

Here's the problem: your brain *hates* that. Remember, there is a finite limit to your memory capacity—four plus or minus two. When the educator starts rambling out bits and pieces of information, the learner quickly experiences cognitive overload, and the amygdala does its thing—routing information to the reactive hindbrain. In this method of teaching, educators are happy if the learners retain even 20% of the information they presented. What a waste of time![3]

EBBINGHAUS FORGETTING CURVE

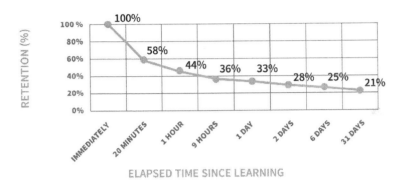

While **rote memorization** isn't inhumane (unlike other aspects of behaviorism), it does seriously impede learning. Think back to the last time you started a new job. Do you remember receiving pages and pages of checklists, action items, and procedures to memorize? How quickly did you memorize it all? It likely took months. Better yet, how much of that information did you actually retain? How much of it can you recall today? Rote memorization does not work within the limits of cognitive ability.

It's important to note that most people don't *intend* to use the behaviorist method. In fact, most people don't intend to use any method at all. They simply mimic how their parents, teachers, and professors taught them. What's more, many parents and educators approach teaching with an intuitive feel. And going with their gut works…at least sometimes. Educators sometimes end up performing what neuroscientists consider the right method by accident (even if it is only partially correct).

Similarly, in the corporate world, a good educator knows that through patience, practice, and observation, doing something one way produces good results. So they arrange their teaching to incorporate it. Yet they also notice that many methods work inconsistently, producing great results with some employees but dismal results with others.

Educators aren't malicious or careless. They simply missed the **cognitive revolution** described in this book's introduction. From a deficit position, relationships between mentors and mentees have almost no choice but to land squarely in the realm of behaviorism. You can't choose another model if you aren't aware that one exists.

However, the educators who free themselves from reward–punishment methods find traction in classrooms where learners are not only engaged and happy to learn but also generate ideas, collaborate, and contribute to their own learning. This kind of agency, **metacognition**, and inclusiveness leads repeatedly to learning with deep understanding. These educators have rewritten their neurocircuitry to think, teach, and learn in new ways... in better ways.

We all deserve the benefit of learning in a cognitive model, where we learn using intrinsic motivation in neuro-aligned models that make sense. The question, of course, is *how?*

*   *   *

BRAIN BREAK: FINGERTIPS

Stand up. Stretch your arms straight out in front of you, tilt your wrists up so your palms are facing you, and cross your arms to make an X. Keep your fingers up in the air and lock your thumbs together. With your index finger on your right hand, try to touch each of the fingertips of your other hand, one by one. Now take the index finger on your left hand and repeat the process. Try switching to use the middle, ring, and pinkie fingers on each hand.[5]

As with previous brain breaks, the objective is to engage all regions of the brain in a simple but energizing activity that increases blood flow to the brain while also connecting the cerebellum, occipital, parietal, and temporal lobes to the prefrontal cortex. In addition, the act of attentional focus, surprise, and shared fun serves to flood the brain's synapses with neurotransmitters that assist the learning process.

PART IV

We All Love A Challenge

4.1

The Educator's Dilemma

Before a facilitator can start educating, they need to understand what it is they want to teach. They usually know what the general topic is and start in the right direction (we call it North-ish), but then need to further refine their thinking as they begin to understand it more deeply. Educators have inherent problems to overcome in a world that is moving fast with a lot of information to relay (beyond being entrenched in a behaviorist model).

Corporate trainers, high school teachers, presenters, and salespeople have an incredible amount of expertise, information, and knowledge to share with others. That's why they're the ones charged with teaching the content. Therein lies the root of the problem—a subject matter expert is often the wrong person to stand in front of a class.[1]

This is because experts can have so much experience that it is difficult to figure out where to begin. Where do you start?

What do you teach first? Imagine a painter instructing a group of aspiring artists. Is the first lesson about line drawing or color mixology? Landscape or portraiture? Most importantly, how does the painter decide what knowledge to share, and when, to inspire these artists to continue painting?

The dilemma is further complicated when you consider that educators are almost always expected to convey the entirety of this information in a relatively short amount of time. It's overwhelming, sometimes impossible—like trying to move to a new house using only one moving box. How do you fit the contents of your entire home into one measly box? Well, you don't. You decide what is important enough to pack in the space available. What treasures do you inevitably leave behind? "It's all important," you say. "I can't possibly choose!"

As a professional in your field, you've likely forgotten what it was like when you first comprehended the subject matter. Your memory has smoothed out the bumps you encountered along the way. You likely can't recollect with clarity what exactly made the subject challenging in the first place.

As facilitators, we can't predict what concepts the learner will struggle with. Each brain is unique. The capacity and composure of each learner is different from the next and different from our own.

For example, consider a mechanical engineer teaching a class on load-bearing roof trusses (those triangular support structures, the plastic parts in your Lincoln Logs set). A builder and a Newtonian physicist sit in the classroom. Each has an expert understanding of the topic, yet they inevitably understand it in different ways. A builder undoubtedly has practical experience with trusses, but might not be able to scribble down the right equation to figure out how much weight the beams can support. Alternately, while the Newtonian physicist could easily solve the equation, they likely wouldn't know how to actually *build* the roof, let alone how to use the dangerous tools and complicated steps necessary to do so. The mechanical engineer teaching inevitably sees the topic differently than both learners. The result might be a failure to accurately predict what skills and knowledge each learner needs for deep understanding.

So how can educators figure out what to teach in the first place?

4.2

What Rich's Daughter And Jeff Bezos Have In Common

Backward design is not new. For many highly organized people and entities, it's a critical method for managing large amounts of concepts and for schematizing events. It's a way to combat major issues that gum up the works for training, learning, and teaching such as too much content, badly organized material, or too little time to deliver it. Many variants of the backward design approach appear in academic papers, publications, and pedagogic tools.[1][2]

We believe that Brain-centric Design's approach is best aligned with how the brain works and how people learn. In it, we accent the important learning elements (what is referred to as the pedagogic content layer) that we know are essential for cognition, agency, and learning with deep understanding.

Our method is called the **nested egg**. It is straightforward, simple, and efficient.

But the best part is that it works every time.

The essential element in the nested egg is the **Big Idea**. We have all invariably asked the question, "What's the big idea?" The Big Idea is a place to logically anchor the rest of the information.

Rich's daughter learned firsthand about implementing the Big Idea when she moved away for college. He tells her story below.

AnneMarie was anxious. It was the day before she left home (Washington state) for her first year of undergraduate studies in Texas. Like most college-bound 18-year-olds, she was grappling with all the new challenges she would face in the fall. In the days before she left, I noticed she wasn't acting like herself.

"What's wrong?"

She looked up at me. I could tell she was ready to spill the beans.

"I'm, like, *legit* stressed out."

"What's stressing you out?"

She thought for a moment. I could see her gears turning.

"Everything! I have to rent a house, I don't know what building my classes are in, I have to move *all* my stuff out, I don't know what my day is going to look like, I don't even know if I'll like it there, I'm worried about Rudy…" The list continued on and on.

I could understand why she was upset. She was moving 2,000 miles away, she didn't know anyone in Texas, and she was nervous about boarding her beloved rodeo horse, Rudy. While she talked, I scribbled down everything that was bothering her.

- Renting a house and paying bills
- Moving all her stuff to a new place
- Boarding Rudy
- Driving 2,000 miles
- Managing the course load

- Being liked by the people at her new job
- Feeling unsure of her new routine

I reminded her that she already had a house picked out to rent and had everything set up with her landlord. She thought about it and agreed that wasn't the issue. The physical act of moving her items wasn't the problem either. We had a U-Haul secured and ready to go, which I would drive, and she would follow in her truck and horse trailer with Rudy, his pasture mate Mandy, and her dog Cheeba.

"What about this last one, then?" I asked. "Are you stressed out about your new schedule?"

"It's just that I don't even know what my actual day is going to *look* like, you know?"

I had finally found the real problem. My daughter likes things to be in order. She prefers to be in control of her life. Her life in Washington was predictable, while her life in Texas was unknown. Her day-to-day routine was a giant question mark.

"Let's make a schedule then."

We spent the rest of the afternoon systematically going through each day. We talked about how she'd wake up at 7:00 a.m. to get to Chemistry 101 by 8:00 a.m. We looked at a map and located the buildings and room numbers of all her classes. We marked out the library and what time the kitchen opened. She copied everything to her new day planner, and color-coded the different aspects for ready view. After a few hours, she had the answer to her real problem.

She had a road map for her new life. The result was that she had a smooth, even enjoyable, transition.

It turns out that Rich's daughter and Jeff Bezos have something in common. They both use backward design to solve problems.[3][4] When Amazon started selling e-books, they did not experience the return they anticipated. Not even close. On paper, e-books were a complete disaster. During an interview with the magazine *Fast Company*, Bezos explained that they had created a product that no one wanted. He stated, "We [had] been working many years, twelve years perhaps, selling e-books, and you needed an electron microscope to find the sales. Nobody came. Nobody wanted them. Nobody needed e-books."[5]

What could the team do? They had poured over a decade of work into e-books. Would they scrap the project completely? Cut their losses and come up with something new? Instead, the team took a closer look at the problem.

Bezos continued, "There are two ways to extend a business. And we do some of both. Take inventory of what you're good at, and extend out from your skills. Or determine what your customers need and work backward, even if it requires learning new skills. Kindle is an example of working backward."

The team asked themselves what the reader needed in order to buy e-books. What was stopping them from reading on the internet? Over time, they realized e-books weren't selling because no one wanted to read *Catcher in the Rye* while sitting at their computer desk. They wanted to read on the couch, feet up, while sipping wine after a long day. Hence, the Kindle was born.

Because of backward design, it's no surprise that Bezos is currently ranked the richest person in the world.[6] Many companies have value statements that include something like "Customers First" or "The customer is always right." But very few companies (almost none) take that statement to heart by working backward from the customer experience.

It may not be easy to locate the Big Idea,[7] at least not at first. In fact, most people like to do a backward design exercise with colleagues and friends before attempting it on their own. However, it's worth the effort of familiarizing yourself with it. Through this process, you can thin down any problem, idea, or concept to reach the heart of the matter. It allows facilitators and teachers to bypass expert blind spots and saves them precious time and energy reviewing extraneous information. Ultimately, it empowers educators to be much more efficient, while also ensuring the information is presented in a learner-centric way.

4.3

What's The Big Idea?

Following are the steps for locating the Big Idea for any information that is being presented.

1. To locate the Big Idea, first create a nested egg. Grab a pen and paper and draw a circle. Label it "BIG IDEA." Draw an egg/oval shape around the circle. Label the egg "Nice to Know."

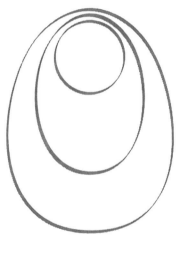

2. Pretend you're teaching a class about the importance of sleep. Ask yourself, "What would I like the learner to know about the topic?" Write those items on sticky notes, one per item. Try to break up long sentences or large ideas into two or more items. The list might look something like this:

- Go to bed at the same time each night.

- Get up at the same time each morning.

- Most adults need 7–8 hours of sleep a night.

- Teenagers need at least 9 hours of sleep.
- Infants typically sleep 16 hours a day.
- Sleep consists of 4–5 sleep cycles.
- Two common sleep disorders are insomnia and sleep apnea.
- You sleep best in a dark, quiet room.
- Exercise daily to enhance the quality of sleep.
- Don't exercise before bed.
- Limit screen time before bed.
- Try something relaxing before bed, like reading or bathing.
- Avoid caffeine, nicotine, and alcohol.
- Anxiety affects sleep.[1]

When you're sleeping, your body goes through several cycles. Each phase of sleep is important and beneficial to your body and mind, but REM is especially fascinating because it increases my activity, promotes learning, and creates dreams!

To a behaviorist, beyond a little tweaking and rearranging, this list would comprise the full presentation. However, if you take a closer look at these items, you will get a whole new perspective. If you went into detail with each bullet on this list, it would take ages to convey all of the information! In addition, based on the cognitive limit of four plus or minus two, this list is way too long. Attempting to review each bullet point in detail will likely push the learners over their learning capacity and into cognitive overload.

3. To "BcD" the info, chunk the content into like categories. Then, in the outer ring labeled Nice to Know, insert the chunked information. It's easy to manipulate concepts since they are already on separate sticky notes. For the sleep example, it might look like this:

- Different ages need differing amounts of sleep.
  - ○ Adults vs. teenagers vs. infants
- Avoid chemical stimulants and depressants.
  - ○ Caffeine, nicotine, and alcohol
- Relax before bed.
  - ○ Try an activity like reading or bathing.
  - ○ Don't exercise before bed.
  - ○ Avoid loud noises before bed.
  - ○ Anxiety affects sleep.
- Avoid bright lights.
  - ○ Limit TV and cell phone use before bed.
  - ○ Sleep in a dark room.
- Have a consistent schedule.
  - ○ Wake up at the same time.
  - ○ Go to bed at the same time.
  - ○ Exercise daily.

1. Now that you've chunked the content, pick out one concept that you believe is the most important for the learner to understand. Yes, just one. This is critical. If you have more than one Big Idea, the learner will be much more likely to end up confused. The crisis revolves around the shape and limitations of the student's working memory space. That's because you're not only constrained by the time limit of the teaching session (whether the allotted time is 20 minutes or 2 days) but also, and more importantly, by the cognitive load of the material.

    Ask yourself, "If the learner only takes away one item from the Nice to Know pile, what should it be?"

2. Place that idea in the middle circle, and label it the Big Idea.

    For this exercise, let's say our Big Idea is "Avoid bright lights."

3. With the Big Idea in mind, ask the following questions:

    - Does the Big Idea relate to Me Here Now?

    - Can I frame the Big Idea in a way that directly relates to the learner?

    - How can I make it more engaging?

    After pondering the answers, "Avoid bright lights" becomes "Why you shouldn't look at your cell phone tonight before bed."

4. Having located the Big Idea, now ask, "What items does the learner need to understand from the Nice to Know pile in order to appreciate why they shouldn't look at their phone before bed?"

5. The rule of four plus or minus two indicates that most learners bottom out at two concepts, so we recommend

choosing two **scaffolding constructs** to assist with processing the information in the working memory space. The scaffolding constructs are two items that are different enough from each other that they require separate processing, but at the same time, both relate to the Big Idea. This pair of constructs will be used to create category labels that help reorganize the basic information into two groups.

6. Label those constructs "Need to Know." They are the scaffolding constructs that support the Big Idea. In this example, these bullet points are the scaffolding constructs:

    A. Limit screen use before bed.

    B. Sleep in a dark room.

A primary benefit of using the Big Idea construct with the nested egg is that it helps prioritize understanding. Think of prioritized understanding as weeding an overrun garden. At first, it's hard to tell the weeds from the vegetables. However, after we begin by removing the crabgrass and move to the clover, eventually the garden takes shape. Through this weeding process, we intentionally pick apart the content and identify the critical pieces of knowledge that the learner has to know for deep understanding. What's more, by changing the Big Idea from "Avoid bright lights" to "Why you shouldn't look at your cell phone tonight before bed," the learner can directly see how the information will impact them—a clear recipe for intrinsic motivation.

A helpful exercise to gauge your success in teaching the Big Idea is to stand at the door as the audience leaves. Ask each learner what they took away from the class. If it isn't the Big

Idea, then you know you need to revise. For example, if my Big Idea was that teenagers need 12 hours of sleep to survive school, yet they said they learned that it's okay to drink caffeine before bed, then my class is an unqualified failure.

Carrying out a similar exercise in the classroom is referred to as formative assessment, where the teacher surveys the students to ensure that what is being understood by the learner is what the teacher had intended. If a discrepancy shows up, it is a clear indication for the teacher that the method or process needs to be adjusted in order to align with the concepts and the learner.

4.4

The Big Idea Produces
Incredible Results

When you catch the flu, you usually visit a doctor's office. Once you shuffle through the door, the doctor asks questions and then types symptoms into the computer. However, they don't type in complaints and medication verbatim. Instead, they enter action codes that represent a diagnosis. The program then sends those action codes to a large database, which processes them and generates a bill.

When you receive the bill, in tiny print on the bottom of the page, you are instructed to call a telephone number if you have any questions. If you call to ask, "Why do I owe what I owe?" more often than not, you're immediately put on hold or maybe transferred between departments. And if you're persistent, you eventually find someone (sometimes management) who can answer the question. The result is a disgruntled customer, a flustered employee, and an overworked manager. All this leads to poor customer service for you, and for the medical company, frequent attrition, a lousy company culture, and a loss of revenue.

In an effort to remedy problems like this, a large medical provider similar to the one described above now employs BcD as a platform for their training. Like many clients, this company thought they knew where the hiccup was. From management's perspective, the issue was that their employees needed help learning how to process claims, which involved memorizing a long list of claim codes over a short amount of time. Because of the call center's high employee turnover rate, management assumed the issue was that new employees couldn't memorize all of the information needed to perform their job quickly enough. But during the Big Idea process, they realized that they had been trying to solve the problem the wrong way.

Management had located *an* idea, but not the right one. The employees weren't struggling with claims. In fact, they were struggling to answer a much different question: "Why do I owe what I owe?" It turned out that over 95% of customers called in to find out the answer to that question. They were shocked or confused by the amount showing owed on their explanation of benefits form, and they needed help to understand the various charges.

Once that question became the Big Idea, the conversation shifted from their reps learning a list of over 60 claim codes to answering one basic question. From this point, we had two scaffolding constructs that supported the Big Idea:

- Action codes
- Empathy

To do their job well, these employees needed to be familiar with the action codes (a separate set of codes from the claim codes) that the physician typed into the database. More importantly, these employees needed to know how to empathize with their customers. They needed to know that it was okay if they didn't have the answer to a question immediately, as long as they addressed the caller's concerns in an empathetic manner and got back to them when they had a suitable response.

The employees had to appreciate that everyone calling was already in (or close to) an amygdala hijack—often sick or injured or with a loved one in that condition—and they were prepared to dispute an expensive bill they might not be able to afford. The customers were stressed out before they even picked up the phone. Once the employees considered who was on the other end of the line, they realized these callers needed someone to say, "I don't have the answer right now, but I am sure this feels overwhelming and frustrating. I want you to get a good night's sleep, so I will call you back tomorrow at 8:00 a.m. with more information."

How often have you heard a call center employee say that? This healthcare company now features one-call resolution, where the employees solve each customer's question in a single call. They may not know the answer immediately, but they do understand what to ask of whom to get that answer.

Identifying a meaningful Big Idea had incredible results for this company. We expected the employees to become better at their jobs once they understood how to answer that question. The employees were trained using BcD, and immediately went from poor servicers to top performers (as measured through more than a dozen statistical and behavioral key performance indicators, or KPIs).

What we didn't anticipate was even more gratifying: the employees began to *like* their jobs more. Despite call centers being notorious for high attrition, at the publishing of this book, the company hadn't lost a single one of the employees who were trained in this model in eight months, which is well below average turnover rates. No external motivators (such as bonuses or benefits packages) produced results like these. We attribute this unprecedented achievement to facilitating a shift in mindset from extrinsic to intrinsic motivation. By understanding how to perform their jobs better, these employees took ownership and became motivated to help the callers. Overnight, "a job" transformed into "my job."

4.5

Educate Like An Orchestra Conductor

Once an educator identifies the Big Idea, they can present it to the learner. However, before they can do that effectively, it's necessary to distinguish between processes and practices that a traditional behaviorist educator uses in the course of delivering to the learners and a BcD, brain-enabled educator who is using the model as described.

Traditional educators often unintentionally get in the way of learning. They make it difficult for their audience by trying to transmit the "right" answer and dinging the unfortunate learner if they come up with a different solution.

In contrast, a BcD educator is like an orchestra conductor. Within the ensemble, there are various specialists (musicians who play the trombone, the viola, the flute, and so on). The conductor does not need to know how to play every instrument—that's the musicians' job. Instead, they only need to know who is playing what, when they are supposed to play it, and what the final composition is supposed to sound like. The conductor leads from a big-picture, higher perspective place. As a leader, the conductor needs skills that speak to each individual, no matter what instrument they play. Within this environment, success is both personal and collaborative, creating an experience that is profound for everyone when they are successful as a team.

Similarly, the successful facilitator creates an atmosphere where there truly is no such thing as a dumb question. They orchestrate an environment where the learner is willing to take risks and step outside their comfort zone. Of course, it is essential that the learner gets to the correct information, gains proficiency, and gives a correct answer if it is required. So simply memorizing the solution to the equation $4 + 4 = X$ has nothing to do with understanding why 8 is correct and 9 is incorrect. Instead, a conversation must take place about why numbers are used in the first place.

Facilitating a deep understanding of the Big Idea generates meaningful discussions, from which innovative ideas emerge. These learning environments fast-track novice employees to becoming experts. Not the typical **routine expert**, but the kind of expertise that is touted for success in twenty-first-century living—the adaptive expert.

Adaptive experts embrace versatility. They are the epitome of cognitive flexibility. Change management is not something they need to learn—they adapt to change naturally and with vigor.[1] These employees can enact change quickly, thoroughly, and efficiently and are able to perform an intricate skill set while keeping the big picture in mind.

Typical corporate models emphasize an opposing view, where unintentional change is the exception to the rule. In today's business world, rapid change is everywhere, and successful organizations are prepared to evolve by training their people, examining existing processes, and using the latest technological tools that make sense.

When BcD works with a presenter or educator, one of the key takeaways we try to instill is flexibility. Educators have to start someplace, and the logical place is with their current teaching materials. Counterintuitively, when we meet, the tools of choice are a pair of scissors and a stapler. We begin by chopping up the materials into one-concept chunks and scattering them in the Nice to Know circle. (Rich typically shows up with his trusty red Swingline stapler as an ode to the movie *Office Space*.[2]) The next step is to restructure the individual topics into meaningful, connected chunks. That's where the stapler comes in handy.

After this process, we commonly see the lights go on. Participants say, "Wow, I've never seen the material presented like this before!" Before long, they become proficient at backward design and begin building new neural pathways to facilitate it. Over time, they are poised to answer the question, "What do I want the learner to remember when they leave this room?"

4.6

The Challenge Wheel

Everything you've read so far is designed to make you a more effective educator. Knowing how neural pathways are created, understanding how to engage strategies of cognitive rehearsal, and being aware of your role in mediating that rehearsal will all enhance learning. It may even make your job easier over time.

Upon entering the classroom, facilitators in the neuro-aligned methods automatically assume that learners are (for whatever outside and extraneous personal and life reasons that have nothing to do with the teacher or the classroom) experiencing an amygdala hijack. They know how to recognize it, and they know to increase dopamine to combat it through novelty, excitement, and relevant activities that mitigate its effects.[1] Furthermore, acknowledging that each learner has a brain with limitless capacity will prompt the facilitator to look for opportunities to exploit plasticity, encourage creativity, and foster agency. Everyone, including the facilitator, will be more patient, empathetic, and collaborative.

However, this information is much easier to put into practice if you have a learning model where the elements of cognition and learning sciences are already built in. That's where the Challenge Wheel comes into play.

The **Challenge Wheel** is a method of instruction that contains a clear, easy-to-use process for arranging content and implementing it. This method is aligned to how the brain works. It is further primed with learning tools like cognitive rehearsal, scaffolded reflection, and opportunities for revised thinking. But above all, it is designed to engage the learner by igniting metacognitive moments, instilling agency, and fostering generative creativity.

The Challenge Wheel takes into account the three basic requirements for all learning experiences.

- Learner
- Content
- Assessment

While these items are related, each one is carefully provisioned by the model, so that the facilitator does not have to think in three separate areas while preparing to instruct or present.

The Challenge Wheel relies on intrinsic motivation by focusing on the Me Here Now of learners and by igniting carefully scaffolded (small- and large-group) discussions that invite individuals into a collaborative, intellectual process. It is intentional about releasing neurotransmitters (like dopamine and serotonin) to ensure that the learner is ready for learning.

These methods are designed to help the learner stay in a comfortable and encouraging learning space where information processing can occur in their executive processing brain regions. The model is cognizant of limits to working memory, and four plus or minus two is a mainstay of the mission so cognitive overload is easily avoided. Finally, through layers of cognitive processing in higher-order outputs, role playing, and argumentation, the facilitator challenges each individual to take charge of their own learning.

The advantages become more apparent with use. BcD streamlines the entire symphony into an easy-to-use process, where the facilitator resembles a conductor of Beethoven's 5th Symphony.

In the **Challenge Wheel** above, we describe five phases that support the Big Idea. Each phase is designed for the learner's maximum engagement while also adhering to the three elements of learning mentioned earlier—learner, content, and assessment. The result is a learning space quite different from the traditional encounter between the "keeper of the knowledge" and passive learners. The graphs on the following pages show how this Challenge Wheel differs from most of the teaching situations we have all endured during our schooling.

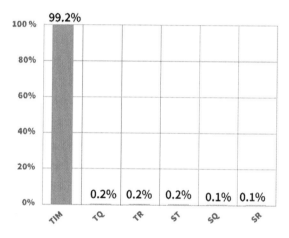

PERCENT TEACHER/STUDENT TALK PER TOPIC
TRADITIONAL LARGE GROUP: MANUFACTURE & TOOLING

TIM = TEACHER INSTRUCTIONAL MONOLOG = 99.2
TQ = TEACHER QUESTION = 0.2
TR = TEACHER RESPONSE = 0.2
ST = STUDENT TOPIC-RELATED COMMENTS = 0.2
SQ = STUDENT QUESTION = 0.1
SR = STUDENT RESPONSE = 0.1

PERCENT TEACHER/STUDENT TALK PER TOPIC
CHALLENGE LARGE GROUP: MANUFACTURE & TOOLING

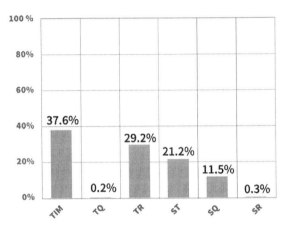

TIM = Teacher Instructional Monolog = 37.6
TQ = Teacher Question = 0.2
TR = Teacher Response = 29.2
ST = Student Topic-Related Comments = 21.2
SQ = Student Question = 11.5
SR = Student Response = 0.3

As is evident from the first graph, in the traditional method, the teacher does 99% of the talking. As a result, students typically listen passively to the lecture without any active engagement towards comprehending the Big Idea or the rest of the content.

In contrast, the Challenge Wheel graph (on the right) describes a cocreation of the learning space where the facilitator and the students acknowledged their preconceptions, reflected on their emerging ideas, felt free to revise their thinking over time, and finally reported out on what the new information meant for them. The learners in the Challenge Wheel model not only learned all of the material with high engagement, they were also responsible for discovering emergent new information that the course creator hadn't even considered.

- The first spoke of the wheel is **Initial Thoughts**. This one-minute phase is designed to prompt learners to engage their PFC instead of their hindbrain.

Initial Thoughts

© BcD Challenge Wheel

- The next spoke in the wheel is **Multiple Perspectives**. This can be any length (depending on how much or how complex the content is) but is usually completed within 15 to 20 minutes. During this activity, the facilitator presents the bulk of the content through multiple engaging resources. Multiple Perspectives relate directly to the Big Idea and comprise an entertaining and consequential opportunity for experts to provide their solutions to the challenge.

Multiple Perspectives

© BcD Challenge Wheel

Reflect

© BcD Challenge Wheel

• The **Reflect** spoke is for the learners to individually process, assimilate, and synthesize the information as best they can, given the amount and complexity of the content. Reflection can be incredibly overwhelming if it is open-ended. For this reason, BcD borrows a scaffolded sequence from earlier learning models that proved how answering three simple questions allowed the learner access to generative and synthesis abilities that work. This novel approach helps eliminate any retroactive inhibitions that might be associated with sharing, competing, or analyzing in a classroom situation.

Retroactive-inhibition occurs when later learning encumbers the memory of previously learned material.

Revised Thinking

© BcD Challenge Wheel

• In the **Revised Thinking** spoke an intellectual cognitive magic takes place. As soon as individuals recognize that other people are listening, sharing, and learning from each other's thinking, everything changes. Eager learners collaborate and compare as they share their initial and reflected thoughts with ease.

Report Out

© BcD Challenge Wheel

• Finally, in **Report Out**, cognitive rehearsal causes neuronal circuitry to strengthen and grow as individual groups share their results with peers in a learning space that has embraced executive function. Here they are generating new ideas and, by taking agency over their own learning, are learning from each other. As participants share what they've learned with the rest of the group, they realize their contribution in an intrinsic motivation space that is tangible and forward-looking.

Emergent thinking and new questions that arise in the Report Out spoke become the new Big Idea, and the wheel starts its next iteration, allowing the presenter to move to the next Big Idea. This time, learners are already primed to expect Initial Thoughts within a safe learning space, and to seek solutions to the challenge as they engage with the Multiple Perspectives. Meanwhile, they are not intimidated by complex or tedious new information.

Depending on the setting and the Big Idea, the full challenge usually takes about two hours. But for complex Big Ideas, it can take multiple days. You can repeat the cycle as many times as you need to and be assured that learners will always be engaged.

4.7

Initial Thoughts:
Prime The Learning Engine

Activity Details

- Allow at least one minute.
- Utilize disequilibrium.
- Prime learner for deep understanding.

Initial Thoughts

❖ BcD Challenge Wheel

On entering the first spoke of the challenge, it's important to approach the classroom as if the learners are already in a reactive freeze, flight, or fight mode. Because people route about 80% of sensory information to their hindbrain, most aren't immediately ready to learn. Instead, they are reacting to the temperature of the room, replaying a discussion with a friend, or imagining what they'll have for lunch. So how does the facilitator engage these learners by down-tempering their amygdala activations and up-activating their prefrontal executive function regions? In other words, how does a facilitator draw in the learner so they are planning, predicting, and thinking about the subject they want to teach?

To combat an amygdala hijack, try activating a moment of **disequilibrium** that connects with the Big Idea. A typical volatile imbalance can be arranged by creating a scenario that is meaningful for the learner (Me Here Now) as they experience a theoretical disaster by doing or saying something that is counter to the Big Idea.

Disequilibrium activates neural circuitry that is associated with arousal, focus, and attention. If you want to engage learners in your challenge, you need to set up a scenario that identifies a crisis if the challenge is not managed correctly. This leaves lots of room for innovation and creative exploitation of real-world phenomena that are attention grabbers. The facilitator who has experience in this model is always on the lookout for items on the news or on the web that will achieve this result for all kinds of learning situations.

In marketing parlance, disequilibrium equates to what can go wrong if you don't do this, the worse-case scenario of looking the other way, the very bad downside of not paying attention. It must be tangible and unapologetic, and the learner needs to feel themselves in this space.

For instance, pretend you've been tasked with teaching new hires at a bank about money transfers. To create a moment of disequilibrium, you might tell them a story about a banker who was asked to move $10 million from one account to another. It was a Friday afternoon and the banker was excited to get home. Accidentally, they transferred the money into the wrong account. Oops! Moments of disequilibrium from the real world get people's attention. And attention is exactly what you need to engage them within the Initial Thoughts spoke.

To begin with Initial Thoughts, employ this process:

- Invite learners to write down their Initial Thoughts about the Big Idea.
- Assure them that they are the only person who will see their Initial Thoughts.
- Allow them at least one minute.

To activate prior knowledge, state the Big Idea and then ask the learners to write down what they already know about that topic. While this activity seems like a small event, it is a crucial part of the challenge. Initial thoughts get learners to do all of the following:

- Lean in and commit to learning.
- Experience active (rather than passive) acquisition of new information.
- Route information to their PFC instead of their amygdala.
- Initiate metacognition.
- Enter a safe learning zone.
- Explore choice.
- Find early success.
- Prime their brain for critical thinking.
- Invite them to make the content their own.
- Encourage them to take responsibility for their own learning.
- Establish a baseline for current knowledge of the subject.

It's essential for each learner to write down their Initial Thoughts. If you ask a group of people to simply think about the topic, many of them will consider it for a mere instant before moving to something else. Or they'll write it off, thinking, *I already know about this topic, so I don't need to think about it now.* Many of us are susceptible to this view, especially in business learning.

The first time you ask learners to write their Initial Thoughts, they might not write anything down. People are often ashamed to write something incorrect (a typical hangover, or retroactive inhibition, from school days). This fear of failure holds back learning. For this reason, the Initial Thoughts activity won't be useful unless the learner understands that it is private, that it will not be graded, and that they will not be labeled or stratified as a result of what they write. If they think they will be singled out or embarrassed because of their answer, they will be hesitant to respond or engage, resulting in difficulty learning.

It is critical that the learners are confident that you, the educator, won't breach that trust. For this to work, they need to feel they are in a safe environment. After a few rounds of the cycle, learners who typically don't write anything down (or write something like "I don't know") will gain enough confidence to document their Initial Thoughts. And this marks a significant transition.

In this moment, the learner moves out of a traditional model based on self-judgment or social pressures where they are afraid of punishments like embarrassment and into a cognitive space where their natural curiosity engages to help them make sense of new information. This kind of agency learning is ideal for deep understanding.[1]

Priming promotes curiosity—and learners' natural tendency to predict—by advertising the content the same way a marketing firm might. By promoting advance interest, the resulting questions increase the learner curiosity and attention toward the Big Idea, so the learner begins to make the Big Idea *their* idea.

Initial Thoughts serve as a reminder of the learner's progress and a baseline for data collection. Writing Initial Thoughts on paper establishes a starting point for preconceptions, enabling learners to see how their thinking has already shifted and how it will continue to shift over time. As the Challenge Wheel goes through a cycle, the learner will be able to literally see their own learning as they gain understanding. This metacognitive imperative enhances learner agency in revised thinking activities, which show up later.

Because the learner is looking for a shift in thinking, it is unimportant whether their Initial Thoughts are correct. **Priming will occur anyway.** Priming is effective for learning when a schema is activated intentionally through a teaching activity that causes a greater response later upon revisiting a similar subject matter.

The critical piece is that by the end of the Challenge Wheel, the learner can say, "I went from here to here. I get this!"

The Initial Thoughts activity of the wheel is the piece that facilitators are challenged the most on, particularly by instructional designers who have cut their teeth on traditional reward–punishment methods. We hear things like, "It's only a minute, so we just skip it," or "We don't have time to write—there's too much information to cover!"

In reality, the small investment spent on this priming activity pays dividends in **metacognition**, agency, **near and far transfer**, and learning with understanding. Transfer is an important construct for learning. If I really get it—if I understand what the new information means—I should be able to take it and solve a similar challenge at a different place and time. Beyond that…if I really, really get it and learn with deep understanding, I should be able to solve a challenge that is dissimilar and do so by using methods and thinking processes that I learned while solving the original challenge. For most learners, this activity is the most important minute of the entire challenge. Priming the learner by activating prior knowledge is tantamount to effective learning.

4.8

Multiple Perspectives:
Experts Engage The Challenge

Activity Details

- Allow 15–20 minutes.

- Present multiple perspectives from various subject experts.

- Use multimedia to increase novelty and remain engaging.

- Maintain Me Here Now.

Multiple Perspectives

⊙ BcD Challenge Wheel

During the Multiple Perspectives activity, experts give their opinion on the challenge by connecting relevant bits of information to the Big Idea via the scaffolding constructs. This spoke comprises the bulk of your content. A typically effective exposition of new content takes roughly 20 minutes. During this time, you present information from various experts to expose the learner to different perspectives. Try to incorporate various kinds of media into this activity to create novelty or to increase attentional arousal and enhance leaning in. Finally, engage the reader by answering the question, "How does this information relate to Me Here Now?"

The content is optimally presented in entertaining and digestible chunks. For example, if you're teaching a group of engineers and your Big Idea is "Why the Apollo 13 space mission failed," your Multiple Perspectives activity might include footage of the launch and subsequent explosion, detailed photographs of the torn-apart machine, and a voice clip from engineers and scientists who built the spacecraft. You could even invite a guest, as long as the speaker is engaging, focuses on the Big Idea, and respects the time limit.

Of course, your Big Idea isn't always going to be as exciting as the Apollo mission. What if you have to train a new hire how to properly file paperwork or present information on the newest technology in vacuum cleaners? Multiple Perspectives are an opportunity for you to engage your own creativity. If you are bored by the content you've provided, the learner will be bored too. Challenge yourself to find and create rich, meaningful content.

Instead of covering the information through a boring traditional presentation, facilitators using this spoke help the learner uncover the new information like magic. How can you uncover the Big Idea by looking through different lenses, mediums, and approaches? True creativity happens here!

Imagine a contractor tasked with teaching the following topic: "How to properly apply paint to the outside of a house using a paint sprayer." That is arguably one of the most boring sentences ever written, let alone taught. Fortunately, this facilitator knows how to use BcD, so they know how to create meaningful content.

After identifying the Big Idea, the painter tweaks the original topic so that it applies to Me Here Now. It's close to the same concept, but now it reads "How to use a paint sprayer effectively so you can spend less time painting." That's getting better. For this Big Idea, they ascertain that the scaffolding constructs are…

- How to correctly calibrate the pressure in the machine
- How to tape up plastic to cover windows and doors

For the first scaffolding construct, the facilitator displays a YouTube video of a technician setting the pressure too high on the machine. The learners watch wide-eyed as stucco flies off the building and lands in the hedge. The facilitator then invites a contractor to tell a quick story about how one of their employees sloppily taped the windows and doors of a house. When the painter pulls off the plastic covering, the edges of the custom stained-glass windows are Eggshell White. The mistake cost the contractor thousands of dollars and took three days to clean up.

The learner can easily imagine themselves in that scenario and make a mental note not to make a similar mistake. With a little effort to engage the learner in Me Here Now, even the most boring topics become memorable events.

Counterintuitively, Multiple Perspectives don't have to be the newest, most accurate snippets of content exposition. They don't even have to be in the ballpark (as long as we're still playing baseball), meaning Multiple Perspectives *do* have to relate to the Big Idea. For example, a key point might be deliberately left out or mentioned lightly in passing to get the learner actively thinking about the Big Idea and cocreating the learning process. Concepts that are inserted at the right time inspire the learner to dig deeper and take ownership of the process. Consider the video of the technician miscalibrating the sprayer's pressure or the story of the painter who destroyed custom windows—they certainly didn't hit the proverbial nail on the head. It is useful to include an example of a multiple perspective that resulted in an unintentional but realistic outcome.

Also, the experts you choose don't have to agree with each other. It can be beneficial to build a little controversy into the discussion. Controversy is engaging—it sparks discussion and appeals to the learner precisely *because* it's controversial. When this is done correctly, a learner can exploit the edges of their experience to construct new thoughts on top of prior knowledge. Sometimes the result is original thinking and creative insight that produces ideas that are meaningful and exciting, and that couldn't have arisen otherwise. Essentially, controversy can inspire original thinking, even critical thinking.

When we approach major companies about BcD, we're often confronted with a particular challenge. Usually, the company has a branded image that they want to use on all their training materials. Fortune 500 companies are particularly fixated in this arena. However, branding may not be conducive to creative interplay in learning concepts. The problem is that it feeds into exactly what the learner is expecting—something produced in-house that looks and feels like their typical corporate brand. But in-house branding is not memorable for most learners. It may have been interesting for the first few months of employment, but over time, it becomes routine. As Brain-centric educators, we prefer to present learners with material that surprises them.

Corporate clients report meaningful successes when incorporating novelty into Multiple Perspectives. For instance, a group of high-level managers from a large international bank in Silicon Valley were invited to tackle a corporate challenge regarding federal compliance laws that forced employees to work from and learn to articulate carefully constructed business requirements. Instead of the usual conference with a bullet-pointed list and a sandwich tray, this facilitator tried something new.

As executives filed into the room, they gasped. It was chaos. The tables were askew and the chairs were splayed out, some tipped onto the floor. The room was freezing. A laptop set to the side of the room was blaring Polka music. The coffee machine was unplugged, and used paper cups piled next to it. Stale cookies from the previous day's meeting were still on the main table. Plates and crumbs were scattered around. No one was there to greet them at the door. In fact, the facilitator wasn't in the room at all.

"What's going on?" asked one manager to another.

After about 10 minutes, the group was so aggravated that they started writing a list to catalog everything that was wrong about the meeting. They weren't trying to be difficult—these managers were simply used to things going smoothly. After a few more minutes, the facilitator entered the room, announcing, "You've just experienced a lack of business requirements. Thank you for reacting exactly as anticipated. This is why it's critical to understand business requirements—so that something like this doesn't happen."

That's the impact of Me Here Now. Instead of telling these managers what they needed to work on, the facilitator *showed* them why it was important. The facilitator made them feel it instead of attempting to understand it intellectually. This is another example of disequilibrium (Piaget referred to this as a moment disequilibrium), when what you expect is not what you get, which can be very effective to keep people in their best attentional space. When used correctly, disequilibrium instantly hooks a learner. They don't just want an explanation—they demand one. The facilitator doesn't want to be a babysitter. They aren't just trying to get through some bullet points.

If you're intimidated by how much effort is needed for the Multiple Perspectives activity, we want to ease your mind. Admittedly, the first round of the Challenge Wheel does take effort on the part of the facilitator, especially when compared to a traditional instructor who might have a clean list of topics to be covered, checks off a box after each one is presented, and calls it a day. However, by the end of the first round of the challenge, you'll step away from the processes, and the learners will take charge of their learning.

For now, just remember you are making an investment up front. While gathering excellent content may be more work initially, it will be considerably less work in the end. Why? Because unlike traditional models, the learner will remember the information provided. That means you'll repeat yourself less without having to revisit old content...or training some of their replacements a few months down the road.

*   *   *

BRAIN BREAK: SIXES

You can stand or sit for this one. Lift your right leg a bit and move your foot counterclockwise, in a circle. Simultaneously, draw the number six in the air with your right finger. It's tricky! After you get the hang of it with your right side, switch to your left. If that becomes easy, try reversing motions to clockwise and drawing the number nine.[1]

4.9

Reflect:
The Art Of Critical Thinking

Activity Details

- Allow two minutes.
- Ask learners to privately answer three questions in writing.

Reflect

BcD Challenge Wheel

As the spokes of the wheel advance, the model invites learners to reflect on new information, which they received during the presentations of Multiple Perspectives for the Big Idea. Reflection is a complicated cognitive function that is largely associated with executive higher-order processing in the PFC. Reflection done well helps learners weigh, evaluate, and synthesize disparate bits of old and new information.

The model scaffolds the learner's thinking with three simple questions designed to further enhance higher-order cognitive processes. The questions are designed to be simple enough that learners won't be intimidated, yet explicit enough to elicit new ideas, activate voice, and elaborate articulation. This portion of the model involving personal reflective practice is useful for arming the learner with words and ideas for sharing their reflections with peers in the next activity.

1. What was surprising?

This question not only helps learners review the content in their minds, it also helps break down barriers and siloed thinking. By answering this question, learners have to take a risk and put themselves outside their comfort zones. Once they do, they often realize that they enjoy the acquisition of new knowledge. It's an easy question. After all, anyone can be surprised about almost anything.

Amusingly, we've found that engineers are typically the most resistant to this question. At first, they hate to admit they are surprised by anything!

2. What did I already know but now I see differently?

This question prompts the learner to consider their Initial Thoughts with respect to the Multiple Perspectives and recognize a shift in their thinking. This is a deliberate metacognitive priming that facilitates sharing, adaptive expertise, and learning with deep understanding.

We often call this question the "bridge." In a piece of music, a lyrical bridge is typically used for listeners to pause and reflect on the earlier portions of the song and prepare for the climax. Just like a typical musical arrangement, the activity of revisiting one's thinking can act as a bridge from what they knew before to what they know now, because of the new information they received.

In other words, it bridges the gap between their old perspective (Initial Thoughts) and their new one (after Multiple Perspectives). It also helps bridge one learner's connection to the next. Knowing that everyone in the room is growing their knowledge while you grow yours opens the learner to the possibility of harnessing the knowledge of those around them.

3. What do I need help with?

This question allows learners to be transparent about what concepts need revisiting in the next version of the challenge. In addition, they often find relief in realizing that other learners are grappling with the same issues they are.[1] If the facilitator has been successful in providing a safe learning environment, people engage in the highly charged process of self-evaluation. The fear of being wrong is replaced by the intrinsic value of bolstering one's own learning through fearless self-criticism and risk taking in front of their peers. Even though most people agree that we learn from our mistakes, many are still hesitant to make mistakes and be vulnerable themselves. Yet vulnerability is essential for conceptual change.

Upon introducing the Challenge Wheel, facilitators are often surprised at just how much learners enjoy this activity. Often instructors will say something like, "We're running out of time, so let's skip the reflection." That idea is usually met with a groan from the learners. What's so special about the reflection is that even though it is short, it is the learner's time to tune out distractions and really think about the content they've just experienced. This is also the time that they arm themselves with relevant verbiage for what's coming next—the Revised Thinking activity.

The Reflect activity of the Challenge Wheel helps to move learners from routine into adaptive expertise. By answering these three questions, the learner is explicitly encouraged to think critically, find their voice so that they can articulate their thoughts in public, and arm themselves for a solid discussion with their peers. In most cases, the cognitive rehearsal that learners experience during this activity is recognized by teachers as ideal for growing mental structures and strengthening concepts. From the classroom to the boardroom, this is critical, because our society demands innovation for future growth. We need adaptive experts in the twenty-first century, and we will need even more of them as our technology progresses.[2] Machines will continue to replace humans through automation, and will subsequently continue to replace routine jobs. In fact, many Amazon employees are actually robots.[3][4] Any employee who isn't a robot will either be replaced by one in the future or is already an adaptive expert.

Imagine teaching someone how to make the delectable dessert crème brûlée. A routine expert, using traditional techniques, would be able to recite the recipe for you. They'd know how long to cook the dessert, what temperature to set the oven to, and exactly how much sugar to add to the mixture. They would be so good at their routine that they would bake a decent crème brûlée consistently.

This chef does well...until something changes and they have to adapt.

Imagine they unexpectedly run out of sugar. Now they are out of their main ingredient and have 20 diners eagerly waiting for dessert. The routine expert would struggle to fix the problem. However, an adaptive expert would adjust to the situation, in keeping with their practiced ability to think critically. They would substitute another ingredient, maybe powdered sugar or brown sugar, adjust the bake time, and leave the situation unscathed and ready for the next challenge.

This is also why we used the term North-ish earlier. Often, we sort of know where we want to go, but we've accepted that along that journey we may have to pivot because of an unforeseen fork in the road. North-ish thinking has a goal, but it also assumes there will be alterations along the way, and leading people through this process will help ensure they will still find their way.

4.10

Revised Thinking:
Activate Choice And Agency

Activity Details

- Allow 10 minutes.

- Conduct as a group activity.

- Encourage groups to share reflections.

During the Revised Thinking activity, small-group peer learners share their reflections. **Role play** is a formative engagement technique for activating individual potential. The model requires assigning several important and meaningful roles that propel the learning while keeping individual learners engaged. Roles typically end up as the following: spokesperson, scribe, timekeeper, and taskmaster. Feel free to make

Revised Thinking

BcD Challenge Wheel

up, add, or subtract roles. It's important to adapt to the learning environment you're in. If the situation calls for it, you may want to switch up the tasks after each round of the challenge so that the activity remains novel and engaging. It also ensures that learners have agency to choose roles and have their voices heard. As learners enjoy the process, they typically self-select into different roles and responsibilities within the group.

Most learners agree that knowing they will have a role is helpful in terms of competitive anxiety and stressors that typically pervade group work. They might not have a role in the first group, but they expect at some stage in the near future to be one of the roles, so there will be no surprises.

Working together in groups is an important part of the challenge. As each group shares their ideas relating to the three questions, learners can see each other's thinking and can learn from one another. This activity sparks new ideas, growth, and a collaborative spirit…and it's fun!

Groups work best with five to seven people, and it is usual to have four or five groups in a typical class. As we tested the model, we were surprised to learn that BcD methods have been successful with groups as large as 500!

It's usually fun for groups to begin their discussion by selecting a nonthreatening name for themselves, typically related to the subject. For instance, a group who was preparing to discuss the impact of stress on learning called themselves the Happy Amygdaloids.

In the activity of revising their thinking, the scribe writes down the main discussion points that emerge as each individual voices their reflection on the three scaffolding questions from earlier. Typically, groups use large sheets of poster paper and color markers so that they can introduce and share their collaborative findings with the larger group in the next spoke of the wheel, Report Out. The timekeeper keeps everyone focused on the work, the taskmaster makes sure that each voice is heard, and by the time each person has shared their ideas, everyone has had a chance to revise their thinking based on new information that was freely given and emergent thought that popped up in the discussion.

There is also provision in the model for individuals who don't want to work with someone else or simply don't enjoy group work. Many people have preconceived ideas about group projects. However, we've seen that by the end of the 10 minutes, their thinking usually shifts. When they see how others respond to the questions, they often gain a new appreciation for their coworkers. This is especially true, if someone can offer an interesting or helpful opinion on the challenge.

We once worked with a learner who wasn't engaged at all during the challenge. His head was down, and he didn't want to interact with the group. However, when the group started grappling with the challenge, another learner leaned over and asked, "Sean, you know about this, don't you?" Uncertain, he didn't respond right away. After a few more minutes, she leaned over again. "Sean, will you please help us?" Suddenly he was engaged. He leaned in and even took charge of the discussion. It was reassuring to observe the interaction.

Every business prides itself on being a team, but when it comes down to it, they are usually just as siloed as every other company. Sure, they'll put people in groups and call them a "team," but the members often remain uncommunicative. The challenge is designed to deliver engagement, especially from individuals who traditionally have difficulty paying attention, following instructions, or working with their peers.

After completing a few iterations of the Challenge Wheel, it is obvious to everyone in the room that the participants have meshed into true team members. They've already established a communication link around the Challenge Wheel with common vocabulary and a tried-and-proven method. This isn't traditional team building. The model doesn't call for trust falls. Instead, we provide a place that invites collaboration and cocreation.

> With BcD, a team is a body of adaptive experts who work together to solve a challenge.

4.11

Report Out:
High-Octane Cognitive Rehearsal

Activity Details

- Allow 10 to 20 minutes.
- Invite a spokesperson from each small group to share their answers to the three questions.
- Provide facilitator feedback.

During the Report Out spoke, learners share their answers to the three questions. The facilitator invites each member to stand while their spokesperson announces the group's name (for example, Happy Amygdaloids) and presents their responses from the Revised Thinking activity. As they present their ideas, each group member will hear their own words repeated, giving them a hit of dopamine.

Report Out

BcD Challenge Wheel

During Report Out, Big Ideas emerge as groups share from every corner of the room. Ideally, the challenge can iterate again with a new theme that emerged from the group discussions. As before, learners will engage, answer three scaffolding questions, and share their ideas with their peer group in collaborative, generative fashion. However, this time the discussion is generated from the learners' own questions. They already know what to do. There are no surprises. They easily achieve and surpass the same level of engagement, buoyed with their intrinsic motivation.

During the Report Out activity, the facilitator will high-light an important transition. As each spokesperson gives their group's answers to the three questions, they will stand and start with the word "we." Before this point, individual learners have been using phrases like "I know" or "I've learned" as they engaged with new thinking and grappled with reflection and revised thinking. But in the Report Out spoke, it is the power of the group that rules the roost. Hearing the group say "we" indicates a degree of safety in the learning space and marks a transition into a collaborative mode. The brain loves to be in the herd, to find safety, and to know that each member is contributing to the social safety of the other.[1]

This activity is highly valuable to the facilitator. During Report Out, you can hear what the learner still needs help with, because you receive direct feedback in real time. Your own blind spots and those of the learners are made visible. If the majority of the groups in the room struggle with the same thing, then your next challenge should be on that topic. It also may signal that you have gaps in your content or that your scaffolding isn't complete or fully accurate. This kind of formative feedback is most illuminating for building better courses and improving learning outcomes.

In this way, BcD helps the learners shift from traditional labeling and stratification in a reward-and-punishment structure to a more brain-aligned approach where higher-order activation takes precedence. Group processes enhance motivation, increase productivity, and foster attention.

In our experience, especially in industrial settings, this kind of group work enhances engagement and allows everyone to enjoy a meaningful learning experience.

What's more, in this model there is no such thing as a "good" or "bad" facilitator—instead you are made aware of how to improve moving forward. If you realize you missed a critical piece of scaffolding to present during Multiple Perspectives, simply go back and insert that piece next time. In this way, you and the learners cocreate the learning experience by working together to generate the next round of the challenge.

One interesting finding is that a facilitator doesn't necessarily need to use the Challenge Wheel in the same way every time. Variations exist. We just showed you the vanilla version. In fact, one of the most important outcomes from using BcD over time is that individual users begin to think in a more cognitive way, using their RAS, their PFC, and their knowledge about the amygdala to better their engagement with their jobs, their learning, and their world.

When put into practice, BcD delivers consistent results. This method offers a new and unanticipated way to acquire knowledge—a better way to learn—that elicits deep understanding of the content. This method reduces attrition in the workplace and increases knowledge retention. More importantly, BcD empowers trainers and trainees alike to find more meaning and value in their work.

This was the case when a BcD team worked with the world's largest shoe manufacturer. As the direct North America consumer services training lead, Ellen worked closely with customer service groups. Her team dealt with any online interaction through the company's website or by phone. It comprised two branches, Quality Assurance and Learning & Development, meaning she offered full-cycle training to new employees.

Like the process at most large companies, Ellen listened to calls, read chats, conducted surveys, and reviewed other consumer interactions. Based on that information, she helped the company decide how well their employees performed.

When it came to customer satisfaction, success was based on these key performance indicators:

- How much time did the employee spend on a call?

- Did they make a sale while talking to that consumer?

- If they did make a sale, how much did they sell?

Before BcD, the trainees would start hitting their target goals at some point between one year and 18 months. As our client complained, "That's like dog years in retail!" Because of the nature of sales, most employees would quit or be moved laterally before they ever got anywhere near their target.

After working with BcD, new hires met that goal within just 90 days! Instead of experiencing overwhelm from items like computer software, products they were discussing, and other nuances of the work situation, these new employees performed like tenured representatives and showed real capacity to solve problems on the fly.

Ellen described BcD as "comfortable and nonthreatening." She reported that for her and her trainees, it was "effortless" and "natural." While most training is tedious and boring, that was not the case with BcD. She also noted that it made so much sense to her in the rearview mirror that she wondered why she hadn't thought of it herself. She went on to say that facilitating with BcD was like "hosting a really great, well-planned party [where] the learners are all your guests."

With BcD, you aren't stuck lecturing. You aren't wasting time and effort on a slide presentation that no one wants to read. Instead, you're helping learners engage in what's happening in the room. You're orchestrating enjoyable, relatable hands-on experiences. You ignite conversations. You marvel as the "proverbial light bulbs illuminate multiple times a day with different members of the class."[2]

Ellen also described an interesting change that one of her attendees underwent.

> A new hire approached me before class. We had been using the BcD method for four days. He was concerned that his level of participation was not meeting my expectations as a facilitator or meeting the level of effort that he was seeing from his peers. He explained that he has social anxiety disorder (SAD). That's why he started working for us in the first place—he wanted a job where he could just focus on his computer screen.
>
> I was surprised that he came forward, because I thought he was doing well in the course. I didn't see someone who wasn't participating—instead, I saw someone who was engaging in different ways through opportunities that didn't alienate him in front of the group. BcD allowed him to be introverted. It didn't cause undesired anxiety or stress. He wasn't exposed or uncomfortable. He went on to tell me that BcD was the best job training he's ever participated in.

Ellen reported that after a while, this young man did feel comfortable enough to speak for his group. Because he was able to get to know his peers and contribute in a way that didn't make him feel vulnerable, he established the level of trust he needed in order to feel confident. As predicted, this young man who suffered from SAD finally found his voice. And he had a lot to say.

Conclusion

Brain-centric Design is real, and this book that describes it is real. We are thankful for the many people who have helped us envision, frame, and deliver it. BcD has been a "thing" for us since we began working with clients who were seeking alternative solutions to thorny issues that plague any workplace. Instructional designers, training managers, and training staff wrangle with the exact same dilemma that we found elsewhere in the learning world. It's the same in large corporations as it is in the elementary classroom—too much material and too little time.

We all have brains. We all learn. In fact, we are hard-wired to learn, but sometimes learning is made so insufferable that the brain can't ignite. In our human capacity, we contend daily with the brain's reaction to the world—a differential neurobiological susceptibility to social context. For many learners, this feels like they are living in a swirling snow globe. A good night's sleep, a little meditation, and voila! It seems as if by magic, the cloudy swirling vanishes and we get a glimpse of a different world. We can see where we have been, where we are, and sometimes, where we are going. At moments like this, we realize simple truths such as the fact that there is not enough love in the world for a golden retriever.

There is a huge gap between being an expert in a subject and knowing how to teach that subject to a novice. That gap is traceable to a paradox in teaching that describes education as the only institution where we never consider the organ that we are trying to change—the brain.

Brain-centric Design is a solution. When these snow-globe problems show up in HR departments (which is very costly for corporate entities) as well as in the home (which is very hard on families), life takes on a much more labored expression. When it gets personal, people take heed.

BcD exists to liberate educators—whether they are corporate trainers, instructional designers, teachers, professors, sellers, or parents—by showing them a new way to teach. A better way.

Once an educator is familiar with the Challenge Wheel, they are immediately more effective at their job. Suddenly they are engaging. Instantly they reach learners who previously said they didn't "like" to learn. They receive direct feedback from each learner in real time, giving them multiple opportunities to modify and improve their content.

Just as our model frees a learner from a stratified, reward–punishment mindset, it frees educators as well. They are no longer seen as "good" or "bad," just like learners are no longer "smart" or "dumb." Instead, educators are the orchestra conductors, playing their role in performing a beautiful composition.

BcD represents many years of research in the field of neuroscience, learning, and training. As the work continues in classrooms, HR departments, and talent development arenas, neuroscience and learning sciences will bridge the gap between educators and employees, ensuring that industries do not remain siloed in their thinking.

Brain-centric Design works in the home, at the office, and with our children. In fact, for it to work, all you need is a brain. For that reason, we can say thankfully that our methods and systems are agnostic of race, age, gender, or culture.

We are entirely thankful for the research in areas of psychology, learning sciences, and cognitive neuroscience that has brought significant insights and accessible solutions to a pervasive and painful learning space. Everyone knows a friend, a family member, a child, or a loved one who has failed to reach their true potential in a world where pain and morbidities seem to dominate their daily existence.

But with Brain-centric Design and knowledge of how the human brain works, we do not need to suffer these negative consequence of who we are anymore. Each day, we are happy to witness amazing changes that are brought about in schools, in the workplace, and in the home.

Brain-centric Design is a fresh and innovative way to enjoy learning in a world that is fast-paced and short on time.

One thing we know for sure is that when learners are given the choice of an engaging brain-centric method versus a traditional memory-centric approach, they immediately perceive the difference and are happy to abandon the old way for Brain-centric Design. Everyone deserves to live in a world where the greatest pleasure in life—learning—is easy, effective, impactful, and enjoyable. Brain-centric Design makes this joy a reality for today's learners and for generations of new employees who are entering the market today.

BcD In Your Industry

Our clients come to us for the neuroscience method, or Brain-centric Design (BcD), which is currently only available from those who have been certified by our trainers as Brain-centric Instructional Designers (BcIDs). These clients understand that our specific expertise is innovative and practical and their needs are typically immediate and ongoing. We understand that both time and output are expensive, veritable money sinkholes.

From managers' point of view, our clients come to us in part because we reduce their sense of risk in the management and effectiveness of employee training. There's the old saying that "Nobody ever got fired for choosing IBM," meaning that choosing a highly respected, visible source for computers is foolproof. We are that kind of low-risk option for improving training's return on investment.

Those who advance to become certified in BcD as Brain-centric Instructional Designers will leverage science in their presentations, classrooms, facilitations, sales proposals, and dinner table conversations with kids and loved ones. The results they experience in classrooms, boardrooms, meeting rooms, and living rooms are often breathtaking. But the real story is how BcD changes the life of everyone who is touched by the knowledge of their own learning, their brain potential, and their place in the world as a result of some new mental models pertaining to plasticity, intentionality, and cognitive rehearsal.

EPILOGUE: On The Shoulders Of Giants

BcD framework is the culmination of decades of science and research distilled into a simple method. Further, the processes and practices described here have evolved over time from many interweaving fields of literature and research. In this way, the end product stems from a breadth and depth of visionary scientific endeavors and outcomes. Without the major contributions of researchers and innovators within many boundary-crossing disciplines, BcD and its connection with modern understanding of how the learning brain works would be nowhere close to where they are today.

BcD owes much to the scientists who, in the 1950s, were aware that the preeminent philosophy underpinning learning and learning systems (behaviorism with a capital B) was not living up to multidimensional claims and, in effect, was an outdated modality for engaging brain and human cognition.

The dichotomous circumstance that followed this realization sparked a cognitive revolution, which consumed the cerebral energies of some of the foremost thinkers and educational theorists of a post-war America that was already in methodological flux. An emergent cognitive revolution delivered a promise of opening up vast new fields of research in areas that connected learning sciences with technology, neuroscience, anthropology, and other related disciplines. Increased sums of research dollars were expended in the pursuit of answers to age-old questions like "Who are we?" and "How do we learn?"

Yet much of everyone else's focus and energy was captivated by sciences in a supreme effort to establish America at the forefront of research in scientific endeavor. Remember, the '50s were a post-world war era, with a Cold War space race in full flight. The nation was captivated by the pursuit of creating and harnessing powerful technologies ahead of the rest of the world (particularly before the Soviets). For example, knowledge that the Soviet satellite Sputnik was crossing over the United States every 96.2 minutes spurred the US government into creating the Advanced Research Projects Agency (ARPA, later adding "Defense" to become DARPA) in order to compete at an international level with scientific projects and military dominance.

Unintended consequences always deliver new directions as a result of historical change. Sputnik had a very subtle but lasting impact on the origin story of the cognitive revolution, dominating as it did—scientific headlines just one year after the fateful gathering of intelligentsia at Dartmouth University. Sputnik, like no other force, inspired an entire generation of engineers and scientists, and did so in a very visceral way. The result was that in between the space race and the Cold War, the cognitive revolution got overshadowed and never made it to mainstream institutions. It settled instead, in more esoteric academic areas like artificial intelligence, neuroscience, computer science, and similar math/science computational fields.

In truth, the cognitive revolution did contribute handsomely to some of these fields, and to advanced theoretical understandings of academic questions like theory of mind, linguistics, and computer simulation using neural networks. In such rarefied intellectual settings, a certain arcane "mystique" became associated with the movement. The accompanying obscurantist view cemented its failure to percolate down into nonacademic facilities and especially failed to find a home in teacher preparation programs or in practical day-to-day operations for business units.

It was a major loss that the cognitive revolution failed to show up on the corporate radar screens of industries grappling with information management, education, training, or talent development. More than 60 years later, the majority of corporate educational systems are still predicated on premodern, Skinner-derived models and behaviorist programs that function with rewards and punishments in worlds of extrinsic stimuli and operant conditioning. As a result, the wisdom and engagement that a cognitive approach engenders are missing in most educational operations, where reactive avoidance techniques dominate corporate learning systems. The mindset of a behaviorist worker that sounds like "I will work hard so that my boss won't discover that I am inefficient and fire me" comes directly out of the playbook of a behaviorist classroom where the student thinks "I will study for this test because I don't want my parent (or teacher) to punish me for getting a bad grade."

Behaviorism became firmly established in learning systems in the US, yet because of the Sputnik effect, ideologies that were popular here spread beyond the shores. Europe was closely allied to the US, and post-war scientific and educational developments that occurred here echoed through countries like Great Britain and France. For the first time, and despite any intellectual divides over geopolitical ideologies, the world seemed to grow infinitely smaller and more connected.

For example, the Jodrell Bank Observatory at the University of Manchester in Cheshire, UK, with its impressive Mark 1 radio telescope, turned out to be one of the few instruments able to track Sputnik's launch rocket as it flew over the US mainland. By sharing information with its close ally, the UK provided much needed telemetry and data for scientific exploration in both countries. Long shadows were being cast.

As scientists and laypeople alike listened to unexpected rhythmic beeps from a tiny extraterrestrial metal sphere, it was clear that the world had reached a new space (pun intended). Clearly, the first artificial Earth satellite was also the first scientific artifact from beyond the planet to unite human thinking about military dominance and survival. In the US, a reluctance to witness the space race from behind caused people to look for deep solutions in areas that related global dominance to advances in artificial intelligence and computational science. Scholars and scientists in this camp were inspired by the burgeoning cognitive revolution and were motivated to forge a path ahead using brand-new methods and models.

It was into this broadening scientific community that a few years later (1978), in a telephone-booth-sized, windowless carrel at the back of the Science Library at the National University of Ireland, that another shadow would be cast. At that time and in that innocuous space, Kieran O'Mahony, then a graduate student in the College of Education, began a research career in relation to long-standing questions in equity, equality of educational opportunity, comparative systems, and modeling methodologies. The carrel was windowless, but it had a deep bookshelf, where volumes of scientists and philosophers spilled out their findings in a way that cast shadows backward and forward and stretched across space and time forever.

In the next few paragraphs, you will meet some of the men and women who shaped the past and cast shadows on the present—men like Comenius, Pestalozzi, Descartes and more whose names are chiseled in a timeless eloquence into decorative roof panels of the Library of Congress in Washington, DC.

Bill Gates knew that it was in this same science library 120 years earlier where George Boole, as first professor of mathematics, had accomplished groundbreaking work in differential equations, but it would be many years before this Boolean shadow would cross his path at Microsoft in Seattle. It makes little sense, except to view it as another edge to a long shadow, to try to explain how a Bill Gates telephony project that would use digital logic and algorithms for connecting wireless devices to the internet could also spill over into learning sciences and equity. But shadows are not grounded in logic. The players who connected AI, learning sciences, neural networks, and ultimately Brain-centric Design were connected, and distributed, at the same time.

Some shadows, reaching forward from ancestral runes, achieve universality—they are not only visible, but are a tangible impact of space over time. For instance, one hundred years before the cognitive revolution in America, George Boole's derivations in symbolic logic and algebraic expression (both computational first principles), provided the theoretical grounding for Bill Gates' world today, and our indomitable information age.

Furthermore, it is no surprise that in 2019 (just as this book was going to press), Geoffrey Everest Hinton, a computer scientist in artificial neural networks at the University of Toronto, was awarded the coveted Turing Prize for his work in artificial intelligence. Hinton, as great grandson to George Boole, epitomizes the marriage of neuroscience, learning sciences, and mathematical computations that expedited machine learning. In one of his acceptance speeches, he outlined the mathematical schema that activates neural circuitry for achieving virtually flawless speech-recognition software using algorithms that are both Boolean and neural. Discussing neural net machine learning, Hinton was explicit:

> The [human] brain…certainly doesn't work by people writing programs and sticking them in your head. So instead of programming it to do a particular task, you program it to be a general-purpose learning machine—a neural net—and then to solve any particular problem like recognizing speech. For example, you show it examples of sound waves and examples of the correct transcriptions of the sound waves, and after a while, it just learns. (Hinton, NPR, 2019)

The cognitive revolution had come full circle. Singularity. In other words, Hinton's groundbreaking discovery was that programming (or in this metaphor, a traditional teaching method) does not work. It is excruciatingly inefficient. This is how he described the achievement of speech recognition software that emulates human neural networks (machine learning).

> All we need to do is figure out how to adapt the connections, because these networks can do anything. It's just a question of changing the connections.

Hinton had unwittingly stepped into the educational side of the cognitive revolution. Though not a learning scientist or an educator in the typical sense (that is, not in frontline classrooms every day), nevertheless, he was finally in BcD territory. Hinton had described the essence of BcD neural nets—we look for and adapt neural connections in a very human way. By iterating through the model, the facilitator will engage and grow neural networks by carefully building and changing circuits, exactly as Hinton described machine learning.

Hinton was perplexed by the apparent dichotomy between human and machine learning. He asked questions that BcD has already answered. Why is the human brain not as efficient as his exquisite, impeccable, all-potential learning machine?

> We were able to accomplish amazing things—the neural net that we create can do anything. With a few billion connections, we accomplished speech recognition in any language in the world. Yet the human brain has trillions upon trillions of connections. So either they are using the wrong algorithm or they are highly inefficient.

I'll say. We are indeed inefficient. Hinton was correct: if only we understood the organ we use for learning, we would indeed be trillions of times more efficient. He is entirely the very apotheosis of a cognitive revolution for education that promised so much but delivered so little.

We fail to reach our full potential, both as teachers and learners, because having missed the cognitive revolution, we are still entrenched in a reward–punishment, social–emotional quagmire with fixed mindset, amygdala hijack, RAS-reinforcing beliefs, and highly suspect mental models that fail to connect with how the brain works.

In the same way that some scientists in the mid-1950s perceived that the prevailing behaviorist psychological models were not meeting the needs of a modern-looking world, many individuals (in industrial settings as well as in academia) arrived at similar conclusions. They came to believe that overtly

behaviorist methods and approaches had them locked into outdated modalities. Skinnerian rewards and punishments were
not working in offices, in workplaces, and especially not for
Human Resources managers who were swamped with expensive efficiency issues that were human derived. Neither were
they working in the home or the classrooms, where bullying,
socio-emotional stressors, and egos were limiting the horizons
of countless children and pushing numerous teachers out of
their chosen field. Some people began to question whether the
behaviorist method ever did work.

But there is always an element of maybe.

It was difficult to write off behaviorism as ineffectual
because for some individuals, whether they are in the workplace, at home, or in school, it simply doesn't matter whether
there are rewards or punishments in the mix. Some individuals
are simply compliant. Their compliance makes them resilient to
the degree that no matter what the world throws at them, they
make it through unblemished.

Their success in the system makes it difficult to spot how
the system fails others. For some, neither rewards nor threats
work. Their resilience levels are intensely connected to rami-
fications of both rewards and punishments so much so that it
costs Human Resources departments a small fortune to manage
their expectations (while costing schools the majority of their
expense), and patience to manage their deficiencies.

All our systems today have been affected by shadows from
the past. For instance, the present national system (K–12) has
its roots in the Napoleonic wars in Prussia 1870s. Big-picture
theorists like Pestalozzi and Rousseau gave us systems and
roadmaps for educating whole generations.

Indeed, Rousseau's *Social Contract* screamed lines that were
to change fundamental thinking systems and societal practice in

a French Revolution first, and then in a sister revolt on this side of the Atlantic.

"Man is born free, but everywhere he is in chains." (Rousseau, 1762)

Rousseau was familiar with Descartes who, as a rationalist, outlined a structure for Cartesian mathematics that your seventh-grade daughter is probably graphing her homework with tonight. He also initiated systems and philosophical underpinnings that connect with Chomsky's ideas of human innateness and universality in today's pedagogies. Recall that Chomsky was a central figure in the cognitive revolution that we missed, and he regards Descartes as the real cognitivist since he, like Boole, laid the foundations for today's scientific and technological world.

Past shadows, sometimes looking like Kuhnian paradigm leaps, stretch forward into modern times. New discoveries and scientific breakthroughs are often accompanied by paradigm shifts that bring solid advances to stagnant thinking and end up changing the way we come to understand our world. Take, for instance, the conceptual change that Copernicus affected. In his time, prevailing best thinking and accepted truisms pointed to a geocentric theory of spacetime. Planet Earth was religiously situated at the center, while all other planets circled strategically around us. It had been that way for centuries. Yet when physical and scientific observations contravene "accepted" norms, when expected outcomes are proven false, scientists do what they do best: they question reality! They theorize new eventualities. They conceptualize different results that lead to a new way of identifying and evaluating observed facts. Having tried new approaches, they make newer, more appropriate assessments and judgments. The results are often as spectacular and resonating as the shift from geo- to helio-centricity. Yet timing is always critical. For Copernicus, it was more prudent to wait till he was on his deathbed before publishing his controversial paradigm-shifting discoveries. And conceptual revolutions are not always the same.

The cognitive revolution of 1956 was quiet and inconsequential by comparison. Nevertheless, the impact was massive, and the shadow that was cast reached as far backward as it did forward. Kuhn and Copernicus were some of the paradigm shifters who occupied the bookshelf of that tiny carrel in the library where Boole had taught. Although imperceptible at the time, many of these colossi of science cast long shadows that affected the outcomes of learning and science for generations. It is easy to embrace the impactful shadow of Boole over Hinton—a blood connection in science and math where an expression stretching from true/false statements in 1849 was central to igniting speech recognition software 170 years later in 2019.

A famous symposium was organized by the special interest group in information theory at the Massachusetts Institute of Technology at Dartmouth University on September 11, 1956.

Several of the scientists who were present and who took part in the discussions and presentations had already made tenuous, shadowed connections back in time to earlier scientists that had pioneered the beginnings of scientific research in their specialties.

On that day, a freshly minted cognitive scientist, Noam Chomsky, presented a paper on theoretical linguistics. He was the first scientific linguist to follow through on systematic theories about language acquisition, by stating with all the precision of mathematics that language acquisition was an innate and universal human capacity. His 1956 paper contained the ideas that he expanded a year later in his monograph, *Syntactic Structures*, which initiated his own rarefied cognitive revolution in theoretical linguistics. Chomsky's contribution to our world of learning today was monumental, but unfortunately for teachers and HR department managers, we missed it.

In 1957, when Skinner published his claims that all learning was predicated on the notion of *tabula rasa* (clean slate, nothing in the brain when we were born) and no free will (all actions are results of external stimuli from the environment), Chomsky was the voice that argued steadfast for sanity. He showed (with his treatise on paucity of stimulus) and observations on language learning in other geographies that children do not learn language the way that Skinner's behaviorism claimed, but rather in a neuro-based argument that pointed to innateness and universality.

Chomsky operated under an elongated shadow of Descartes, who—as rationalist and philosopher—reached forward to like-minded rational thinkers with his conceptualizations regarding mind and matter. He was one of the first people to conceptualize the notion of innateness for language acquisition. Chomsky took this to a new level with his theories on syntactic structures and linguistic constructs of universality and internalism. Most scientists rallied around Chomsky, who was one of the most vocal scholars against extant behaviorism, and who decried Skinner's writings as amounting to nonsense.

It was at this same conference that George Miller presented his amazing paper, "The Magical Number Seven Plus or Minus Two," which was showcased as a polemical nugget on how humans could avoid the bottleneck created by a limited short-term memory. Many years later (2012), he admitted that this paper surprised him for the shadow it cast and the impact it would have on fields as diverse as telephone numbers and learning science.

Miller was also influenced by a faint but connective shadow that was cast by the great medieval medical virtuoso Vesalius and his predecessor, the Roman scholar Galen. These medical scholars and practitioners were first to theorize that cognition and memory were functions of the brain. Miller, Vesalius, and Galen held a revered space on that bookshelf right next to Copernicus, Pavlov, and Skinner. And today, functional localization, Miller's Law, and Hebbian theory are critical mainstays of BcD methodology. Donald Hebb was not in that carrel and didn't show up until Skinner fell out of favor.

IBM and neuroscience might have seemed like strange bedfellows back in 1956, but Hebb's postulate, relating to work on neuropsychological theory of cell assemblies, demanded a computational memory capacity worthy of the best computer in the field at the time. Hebb too, was influenced by the foundational work of a shadowed historical figure, Franz Joseph Gall, whose controversial work on phrenology didn't stick, but whose brilliant observations on functional localizations are amazingly accurate to this day.

The cognitive revolution was substantial in affecting change in several interrelated fields of science and artificial intelligence and has only lately made its way into teaching, learning, and human cognition. The scholars who were present at the conception and who ignited a generation of learning in their respective fields contributed to technological advance and modern theoretical and conceptual spectra of social advance Yet it seems strange that the areas that stood to benefit the most had to wait the longest.

John Bransford, a research scientist who achieved fabulous work in learning sciences at Vanderbilt and later at the University of Washington's LIFE Center (Learning in Informal and

Formal Environments) contributed more than any one individual to this evolving situation.

Bransford arrived at the university of Washington around the time O'Mahony was planning on walking out. They hadn't met yet. O'Mahony had been studying learning systems and cognitive processes for over a year, with frustration compounding every month he was there. Despite everything he had learned about how information is processed in the prefrontal cortex, in spite of all of the research available on how stress affects the amygdala and the role of cortisol and dopamine in the learning process, and regardless of the underwhelming results educators continued to see in the classroom, most professors still used the behaviorist method to teach.

Luckily, Patricia Wasley, dean of the College of Education, was more flexible and tolerant than he. When he told her he wanted to drop out of the program, she said, "Wait. First, you have to meet Dr. Bransford."

John's long career in cognitive psychology and learning sciences contributed to groundbreaking events at many institutions. In the years leading up to the turn of the century, together with colleagues and grad students, he pioneered learning sciences work with a program called JASPER (joint attention, symbolic play, engagement, and regulation), which brought together experimental psychology, technology, learning sciences, and cognitive studies. The field expanded in several facets of learning sciences and emerging technologies but settled on a cognitive construct that became known as anchored instruction. Out of that research came the genesis of the challenge model, which in turn morphed into the theoretical underpinning for Brain-centric Design.

In the early 2000s, the LIFE team began a research project to investigate the impact of an emergent cognitive model compared to a much-used traditional method of teaching in adult learning settings. In an informal experiment, they tested both models on an engineering complex where modern manufacturing techniques were being pioneered. They used the same content but presented it in two different ways. Results were illuminating, resulting in several pedagogic breakthroughs that shaped the methods used in many K–12 sites today.

The cognitive revolution had finally arrived in the world of adult learning.

Traditional educators are particularly mindful of the "3Rs"—reading, (w)riting, and (a)rithmetic—a pronounced tongue-in-cheek play on the sound of learning. Notwithstanding the overriding focus on promoting proficiency in these three critical areas of academic achievement, all relevant agency data (from the National Association of Educational Performance or NAEP, US Department of Education, and Trends in International Mathematics and Science Studies or TIMSS) inform us that proficiency has been at a dismally underperforming standard for the past 50 years, with no discernible improvement on the horizon. Despite their best attempt, it appears that many educators have failed to deliver on the 3Rs.

When searching for a cause of that failure, we are reminded of the old dean who remarked of the cognitive students, "There is so much chaos in your class that the students couldn't possibly be learning anything!" To equate compliant quiet with learning is a mistake that is easy to make, but a mistake nonetheless. In fact, the louder the room, the better.

The fact that schools continued to underperform amidst available neuro-aligned methods always bothered Dr. O'Mahony. How could it be that in the most advanced country in the world, and after a dozen years of schooling, young people could emerge with such dismal results? It didn't add up! For O'Mahony, asking the question was revealing and finding the answer was mind-blowing. It wasn't the brains...it was a deep-rooted commitment to an outmoded methodology that basically consigned learners to a reactive freeze, flight, and fight learning zone. As reported earlier, the behaviorist reward–punishment model works okay for some of us (if we have sufficient resiliency and are able to withstand the drudgery). But for the rest of us, it is an ineffective course of action with low success.

However, when the game changes, a new sound of learning can be heard. When behaviorism is replaced with a new understanding, everything changes. For modern teachers, learning occurs when neurotransmitters are released by a presynaptic neuron, which in turn influences electrical activity of a postsynaptic neuron, and an action potential propagates an electrical current to activate a particular circuitry—the sound of learning is different. It changes from repeat/cram/regurgitate to action potential/circuit/propagate, and this is achieved with reflection/revised thinking/report out.

When a learner listens to the synaptic symphony going on inside their head, it changes the way they learn.

With Brain-centric Design, the new 3Rs—Reflect, Revised Thinking, and Report Out—define processes and practices that change that original and outdated paradigm. Paradoxical and delightful outcomes emerge. Even though the focus is not on reading, writing, or arithmetic, these same proficiencies improve, along with a learner's capacity to grow intellectually, socially, and emotionally. The simple measure of connecting neuroscience with teaching and learning invokes a paradigm shift in attitude, mental models, and intention for both the teacher and the learner.

When the brain is in its element, it knows what to do—learn.

A Note From The Authors

Knowledge is only powerful when shared. Given this, we hope that future generations of educators and scientists will stand on the shoulders of this work, and in doing so, will further perfect this approach to learning and the brain.

Acknowledgments

~ Dr. Kieran O'Mahony

We are grateful for the help and support that many individuals and organizations have contributed to the creation of this work. Gratitude is central to cognition and neuroscience, a core function of neurobiology that activates the limbic system with emotional and empathetic overtones. Countless studies endorse the idea that a simple act of gratitude can change our lives and change our place in the world. Gratitude makes sense to the fulfilled brain.

Here we would like to include some of the amazing people who have contributed to the journey of Brain-centric Design. It was not an overnight success as we would like to claim, but years and years of struggle against a system that was obviously not working and one we were trying to accommodate. There was no one flash of recognition but rather a slow dawning that we were beginning to think differently. There were just too many coincidences in the new method that pointed out that in the recent past, all our efforts and energies had been foolishly expended in simply rearranging deck chairs on the *Titanic*.

The strange clarifying moment was when we suddenly realized we were not even on the Titanic anymore. We had abandoned ship and were rowing away speedily, putting as much distance between us and the spiraling hulk circling its death dive as we could. We are thankful for the many life jackets that we found along the way.

Brain-centric Design was fortunate in finding Thanet House Books; it was a serotonin moment. As a best-selling author, Julie Anne Eason was the perfect leader to drive a project as all-encompassing as the human brain and the human condition. A deep thanks to Julie and her amazing team for embracing the breadth of this undertaking, bringing energy and drive to see it through. Thanet House is indisputably invaluable to publishing and authorship.

In particular, the many nuanced skills of a writer like Michelle Stampe, who is equally at home on a fat bike as with a fat sentence—a true dopamine experience. We are appreciative of her skill with dangling participles and her gift for making the pedagogic and cognitive bearable and accessible.

Meanwhile, Kevin LeBlanc is a master at herding cats, leading the norepinephrine squad. There are so many loose ends, hanging chads, and unknown impending dooms that even the most together person should feel perturbed. But not Kevin! We are indeed inherently blessed by his presence on the Thanet team.

Likewise, managing editors are gifted and truly adventurous spirits. We are fortunate to have had the privilege of working with the best. Julie Willson ("the other Julie") held us accountable to writing timelines, provided timely words, and offered encouragement as the project evolved.

We are fully aware that this book is the better for the Thanet House team's attention to detail, their skill in managing authors, and their support in the creative process.

When one finds the perfect graphic artist, the work comes alive. We are grateful for the assistance of a team of design and graphic specialists who have contributed to this work. Geoff Neil is a skillful and amazing artist who turned a conversation piece about a concept into a fabulous art form. Late to the team but talented and expressive is Gabriele Bonavera, whose Italian penmanship comes from a heraldic era where masterpieces abound.

We are indebted to everyone on the cutting-edge team of artists, analysts, and business specialists who have propelled the strategies and methodologies of BcD into the marketplace with great success. DeAnne Moore is a numbers person who keeps the cogs spinning without missing a beat. Diorella Pugliese, with her Latin energy, manages the processes so that even Asana knows what is going on. David deVarona is a classic example of just-in-time expertise—straight out of college and already immersed in a thriving life change.

Particular individuals contribute in areas that are esoteric and inspiring. A growing body of evidence suggests that the presence of real artifacts of precious art in a learning space engages the learner in an emotional, inspirational, and creative way. Art and inspiration are critical for science as well as for writing. This book is a blend of both.

We are grateful for the continued friendship of Mike Peck for his vision, patience, and generosity with respect to artistic delights in time and space. From a neural perspective, inspiration is tricky; when it is lacking, the motivation to learn, adapt, and prosper suffers. As an integral aspect of the artistic experience, it involves integration of higher cortical circuitry and deep brain structures such as the limbic system and medial frontal structures, which enhance the appreciation of the esthetic. Mike's contribution to Brain-centric Design is quietly inseparable from his artistic nuances and ceramic suggestions. A huge study in gratitude!

Neuroscience should always have been central to learning systems. In hindsight, it's easy to see that. But when the insights were becoming clearer, several individuals were quick to make the jump. Traditional methods were stretching their patience and their sense of equilibrium as they engaged in the heady tasks of delivering important information to people who were essentially not able to accept the cognitive load. One of the early adapters of this cognitive approach was Melissa (Missy) Widmann, who immediately became its most vociferous and assiduous proponent. I am very thankful for Missy's enthusiasm, support, and perspective. As an amazing teacher, she brings the neuroscience method to valuable fruition every day in her work with teenage learners. I am grateful also for the efforts of Ashley Valentine, Christine Young, and Jerome Hunter, all of whom are delivering change in a dramatic way every day to K–12 systems and children. If you want to see the neurotransmitter oxytocin in action, just attend an activity where these amazing practitioners are holding court.

Without the children who are impacted by this work, our world would be very bleak. Some of us began in the classroom and feel at home there. Thankfully, we get to spend a great deal of time each week in classrooms. To the amazing children in whom we witness agentic learning and aha moments, we are forever grateful. There is always a Madelein in the room. There is always a Jackson in the room. At the confluence of learning and music, there are always a Noel and a Ronan. Some kids are so intense and will always give more than 100%. Yes, there is always a Shane in the room. You have no idea how much you mean to this changing world. Finally, we are eternally grateful for Ms. Techtite for her vision and endurance. Katie is guaranteed to show up with as much excitement as a possum at a trash heap.

Music contributes to the part of the brain that brings attention into focus. It enhances a person's ability to make predictions and increases working memory so that learning is enhanced and retention is optimized. For this reason, all BcD classes are musically alive, engaging, and generative. If you are in a BcD class, you will be contributing to a verse or a round in some way. I am indeed thankful for the merging of methodologies that includes music, art, and higher-order processing with executive function so that we achieve learning with deep understanding.

Acknowledgments

~ Rich Carr

My Teachers
Phil Langston

My high school English teacher was the one who triggered the love of writing in me when, instead of writing about capital punishment or Roe vs. Wade, he let me write a comparison and contrast paper on KISS vs. The Bee Gees. I received an A, but it wasn't the grade that motivated me. When he handed the paper back, he said, "You know, you can make money writing like this." He then told me about *Writer's Market*. I queried *Spin Magazine*, and they printed my first paid gig on Motley Crue's *Theater Of Pain* and numerous others. I've been writing ever since. For me, Phil Langston was that teacher who changed everything.

An interesting side note: Years later, I participated in a celebrity golf tournament and was paired with Vince Neil of Motley Crue. I asked if he ever read the review. He hadn't, but asked what I wrote. I told him I hadn't been that kind, especially about the song "Home." He laughed and told me he had written the whole album sober while in prison and that he thought it sucked too. The album reached #6 on the US charts and #36 in the UK and was certified quadruple platinum by the RIAA on June 5, 1995. (He's a great golfer, BTW.)

Roger R. Reynolds

Former Disney voicework artist turned college professor, Roger was another teacher who let me explore. Mass communications and electronics were my passions in college, and with Roger as my advisor, we made the college radio station (KCAT) a real workplace and a cool thing. It was my first taste of radio leadership, and I went on to own three different radio stations, achieving heights never imagined. Roger also drilled a phrase into me during voice and diction classes that my kids joke will be on my epitaph: "You must speak as crisp as lettuce." He was also a champion duck caller.

Roy H. Williams

Roy is the founder of The Wizard Academy in Austin, Texas, as well as a *New York Times* best-selling author of the *Wizard of Ads* trilogy. He's been a great friend, mentor, and advisor and somebody I could always lean on for a nudge towards my Northish Star. Roy solidified my leap from the corporate world to my own business, challenged me to write better advertisements and marketing materials, and introduced me to the idea that the brain could be a useful tool if you knew how it worked. He showed me that *Don Quixote* was the one book I could read and/or listen to several times over and each time find or feel something new in its prose and in myself. Broca's Area started it all for me.

My Leaders
Sue Giovanni

This tiny Italian fireball ignited me in personal growth, motivation, and schemas. My sales manager in two different positions, one in Nashville radio and another in a national video marketing service, Sue turned me on to neurolinguistic programming, the fact that sales aren't the sales widely reported but a service to assist, and that a good party is well deserved when appropriately timed.

Bill Ashenden

Bill is the world's greatest manager. My direct supervisor at Paul Allen's Rose City Radio Group, where I became the Director of Digital during the birth of the internet, Bill challenged, mentored, and friended me and made me into a leader who could communicate and not just direct. He was fair, ethical, goal-oriented, and ever exploring opportunities, and I try to emulate his leadership daily.

My Innovators

Jason Clement

A true visionary in business, Jason applauded the move to cognitivism in the workplace, and he understood the power of music and the value of not taking the same path that didn't work before. He kept a sharp focus on results and was the first to really put Brain-centric Design under the assessment microscope with 15+ KPIs of before-and-after results at a global level. Business aside, he's open and inquisitive, loves a good jingle, and is fair to everybody while being very clear about his needs and intentions. He is a joy to work with, as he instills the desire to achieve at higher levels on multiple planes.

Peter Vultaggio

Peter reached out to Brain-centric Design after a blog post I wrote many years ago about Miller's Law called "Chunking." Since then, he has onboarded us into two large industries and brought staff on two continents into the cognitive shift through training, speaking engagements, and numerous configurations of the model. His direct leadership style is friendly and fast, and he always strives for the best results.

Jeff Chandler

Jeff first hired my firm when he was running The RAM, C.B. & Potts, and Humperdinks restaurants throughout the United States. He later brought my firm into the Young Presidents' Organization and many other endeavors. Currently leading the country's top burger franchise, HopDoddy Burger Bar, Jeff once invited me to stay in his villa in Italy for the experience of a country that has got culture down to an art form. We're still great friends, and I completed this book while staying in another villa in Italy, thanking him every day as I breathed the air, saw the colors, and walked where DaVinci had.

MJ Jordan

Bold and visionary, MJ was the first to lead Brain-centric Design to a global audience with jaw-dropping success. From our earliest collaborations, her adaptive expertise was always on display, and the retail manufacturing giant for which she manages the learning and development team is leading the world in innovation. Not a coincidence!

Daniel Whittington

Depending on where you look, Daniel Whittington is either a musician, bookkeeper, whiskey sommelier, or somebody in a constant mode of creation. Daniel gave The Wizard Academy stage to Brain-centric Design in its earliest form, attracted people from several countries to attend, and we've been igniting brains ever since. Thank you, Daniel.

Darian Rae Andreula

A most talented, insightful, and willing-to-be-placed-in-any-position-asked type of person, Darian once served as a "mole," gathering intelligence from deep within a learning community (as a part of it), delivering key insights that had before been impossible to gather. Working with her made BcD credible and effective immediately and forevermore.

Duke Moscrip

He's known as an iconic restaurateur in Seattle for his Duke's Chowder House chain, which has served and promoted sustainable seafood for more than 30 years, but he's really one of the world's greatest facilitators and critical thinkers.

Glossary

action potential: An electrochemical wave, which travels along the axon of a neuron. When the action potential reaches the presynaptic terminal, it provokes the release of a small quantity of neurotransmitter molecules, which bind to chemical receptor molecules located in the membrane of the postsynaptic neuron on the opposite side of the synaptic cleft. The wave of depolarization along the axon is called an action potential.

adaptive expert: A broad construct that encompasses a range of cognitive, motivational, and personality-related components, as well as habits of mind and dispositions. Generally, problem-solvers demonstrate adaptive expertise when they are able to efficiently solve previously encountered tasks and generate new procedures for new tasks. Requires an individual to develop conceptual understanding that allows the "expert" to invent new solutions to problems and even new procedures for solving problems.

amygdala hijack: An immediate overwhelming emotional response with a later realization that the response was inappropriately strong given the trigger; responsible for the freeze, fight, or flight response that results as a person responds to threats.

amygdala: Central structure of the limbic system attached to the tail of the caudate nucleus. The amygdala is involved in emotion and is responsible for changes in mood and emotions, including rage and aggression. It is important for learning since it associates objects with reward or punishment. The amygdala is also a key structure in processing fear.

attentional arousal: How we actively process specific information present in our environment; what we attend to; a process in which a person pays attention to specific information connected to attentional capture and working memory space.

axon terminal: Where one neuron transmits a signal to another neuron's receptors by changing the electrical signal into a chemical signal called a neurotransmitter.

axon: A long threadlike part of a nerve cell that facilitates communication. Electrical impulses are conducted away from the cell body to other cells. Although each neuron can have only one axon, the axon itself can have many branches, which connect it to many others. Myelinated axons are known as nerve fibers. The function of the axon is to transmit information to different neurons, muscles, and glands.

backward design: Based on philosophic underpinnings of critical thinking and managing large amounts of information so that chunking, agentic learning, and cognitive rehearsal are enriched.

behaviorism: Psychological theory that behavior can be explained in terms of conditioning, without appeal to thoughts or feelings; only concerned with observable stimulus–response behaviors. Behaviorists believe that all behaviors are learned through interaction with the environment.

Big Idea: Emanating from a backward design philosophy, this outlines the enduring idea that the learner takes away after the pedagogic experience.

brain stem: Forms the connection between the brain and the spinal cord; maintains vital control of the heart and lungs and coordinates many important reflexes.

cell body (soma): The factory of the neuron; produces all the proteins for the dendrites, axons, and synaptic terminals and contains specialized organelles (such as mitochondria) to provide energy and make the parts, as well as a production line to assemble the parts into completed products.

cerebellum: Located behind the top part of the brain stem (where the spinal cord meets the brain); made of two hemispheres (halves); contains roughly half of the brain's neurons, specialized cells that transmit information via electrical signals; receives information from the sensory systems (touch, sound, smell, etc.), the spinal cord, and other parts of the brain and then regulates motor movements (walking, running, lifting, etc.); coordinates voluntary movements such as posture, balance, coordination, and speech, resulting in smooth and balanced muscular activity.

Challenge Wheel: Iterative pedagogic model that engages learners so that agentic capacity is enhanced.

chunking: A process by which individual pieces of information are bound together into a meaningful whole.

classical conditioning: Automatic reflex (like a dog salivating for food) is associated (paired) with a meaningless stimulus (a metronome) so that the one stimulus elicits the response from the other stimulus (metronome chimes and dog salivates); limited when it comes to shaping behavior, because an automatic response must already exist.

cognitive load: Capacity of working memory to process new information.

cognitive overload: Occurs when we reach the limitations of working memory; if there is too much information, the learner is unable to process it, which produces anxiety and stress.

cognitive rehearsal: Intentional repetition that is aligned with how the brain works and how people learn.

contralateral: The other side; the opposite of ipsilateral, which refers to the same side. In the human brain, regions in one hemisphere control movement and actions in the opposite side of the body (the right eye is processed in the left occipital lobe visual region). For example, a stroke involving the left side of the brain may cause contralateral paralysis of the right hand.

corpus callosum: Largest white-matter structure in the brain, consisting of 200–250 million contralateral axonal projections, and the major commissural pathway connecting the hemispheres of the human brain; responsible for integration of information between left and right cerebral hemispheres.

dendrite: A short-branched extension of a nerve cell, along which impulses received from other cells at synapses are transmitted to the cell body.

dendritic arborization: A tree-like branching of dendrites that facilitate new synaptic connections.

dopamine: A neurotransmitter that helps control the brain's reward and pleasure centers; helps regulate movement and emotional responses; enables us to not only see rewards but also to take action to move toward them.

emotional arousal: Mental reactions that are expressed such as happiness, sadness, anger, and hopefulness, which play a huge role in how humans behave individually and socially. The amygdalae are responsible for preparing the body for emergency situations, such as being startled, and for storing memories of events for future recognition.

executive function: Mental processes that enable one to plan, focus attention, remember instructions, and juggle multiple tasks successfully; ability to filter distractions, prioritize tasks, set and achieve goals, and control impulses.

extrinsic motivation: Behavior that is driven by external rewards like money, fame, grades, and praise; when behavior is motivated by an external factor influencing a person to do an activity in hopes of earning a reward or avoiding a less-than-positive outcome.

fixed mindset: Underlying beliefs people have about learning and intelligence; some people believe their basic qualities such as intelligence or talent are fixed traits.

flight, fight, freeze mode: A body's automatic, built-in system designed to protect one from threat or danger; critical to survival from real danger; for a lot of learners, anxiety can also trigger this system when they believe there is a threat or danger, even if there is not.

forebrain: Largest part of the brain; located near the front; includes the cerebral hemispheres, the thalamus, and the hypothalamus; controls body temperature, reproductive functions, eating, sleeping, and the display of emotions.

four plus or minus two: Revised limitation to working memory, from Cowan revisiting Miller's original research (seven plus or minus two).

frontal lobe: Region of the brain immediately behind the forehead; includes areas related to behavior, learning, personality, and voluntary movement.

growth mindset: An underlying belief people have about learning and intelligence. When students believe they can get smarter, they understand that effort makes them stronger. Changing one's belief from a fixed to growth mindset leads to increased motivation and achievement.

Hebb's Rule: A neuroscientific theory claiming that an increase in synaptic efficacy arises from a presynaptic cell's repeated and persistent stimulation of a postsynaptic cell; an attempt to explain synaptic plasticity, the adaptation of brain neurons during the learning process; often expressed as "neurons that fire together wire together."

hindbrain: Lower part of the brain stem comprising the cerebellum, pons, and medulla oblongata.

hippocampus: Elongated ridges on the floor of each lateral ventricle; contributes to processing emotion, memory, and the autonomic nervous system.

homeostasis: Body's natural tendency to seek equilibrium. An organism's behavior is determined by the way it senses and perceives the surrounding environment and by its responses to stimuli. Factors that affect the behavioral response to an event include genetic background, environment, past experiences, and their imprinting on the relevant brain circuits.

Initial Thoughts: A spoke of the Challenge Wheel where the learner leans in, engages with the challenge, and by predicting a solution, engages the executive function of the prefrontal cortex.

intentional practice: Purposeful and systematic exercises beyond mindless repetition; requires focused attention and is conducted with the specific goal of improving performance.

intrinsic motivation: Behavior driven by internal rewards; the perception of an activity as an opportunity to explore, learn, and actualize one's own potential.

Me Here Now: Attentional aspect of learning; learners believe "If it's about me here and now, I'm in."

mental model: Representation of concepts, frameworks, or worldviews that one carries around in the mind; thinking tools that one uses to understand life, make decisions, and solve problems.

metacognition: Thinking about thinking; knowledge about one's own information processing and strategies that influence one's learning that can optimize future learning. When individuals are prompted to think about, articulate, and/or reflect on and recognize successful learning strategies, that reflection can reinforce effective strategies.

midbrain: Topmost part of the brain stem; associated with vision, hearing, motor control, sleep/wakefulness, arousal (alertness), and temperature regulation.

Miller's Law: Research by George Miller that tried to define the limitation of human working memory where its span was not limited in terms of bits but rather in terms of chunks; featured in a 1956 paper (from the cognitive revolution) entitled "The Magical Number Seven Plus or Minus Two."

Multiple Perspectives: A spoke of the Challenge Wheel where the facilitator presents information delivered by experts to illuminate the challenge under investigation.

myelin sheath: Protective insulation of a nerve that accelerates impulse conduction; when it is damaged or disappears, the conduction of impulses along nerve fibers slows down or fails completely and brain functions become hampered or are lost.

myelin: A fatty substance that wraps around nerve fibers.

myelinated: The condition where a nerve is coated with myelin, increasing the speed at which impulses propagate; along unmyelinated fibers, impulses move continuously as waves, but in myelinated fibers they "hop" or propagate by saltatory conduction.

negative punishment: In operant conditioning, removing something pleasant to influence behavior. For instance, a teacher might take away a pleasant consequence (such as free reading time) from a student in order to discourage their maladaptive behavior (playing games on his phone during class).

negative reinforcement: In operant conditioning, removing something noxious to influence behavior. For instance, a teacher might take away an unpleasant consequence (such as detention) from a student's schedule in order to encourage that student's good behavior (studying hard for a test).

nested egg: A model for facilitating a thinking system that aligns with how the human brain works and how people learn best; structured to resemble an egg with an oval shape containing a circle that has the Big Idea.

neural circuit: Neurons that perform a function connected in a pathway; carries information from one point in the body or nervous system to another; uses electrical and chemical energy to carry information along a path.

neural networks: Connections between neurons; a fundamental unit of the nervous system. Without communication between neurons, no complex behavior or thought would exist.

neurons: Specialized cells in the brain and throughout the nervous system that conduct electrical impulses to, from, and within the brain; composed of a main cell body, a single axon for outgoing electrical signals, and a varying number of dendrites for incoming signals in electrical form. There are up to 100 billion neurons in an average adult brain.

neuroplasticity: Adaptability of an organism to change in response to its environment; one of the primary attributes of learning, which results in students gaining agency over their own education.

neurotransmitters: Chemicals that transmit signals across a synapse from a firing neuron to a target neuron; released into the synaptic cleft, where they are received by receptors on other neurons; play a major role in shaping everyday life and functions; exact numbers are unknown, but more than 100 chemical messengers have been identified.

novelty: When something that is new, original, or unusual grabs our attention for long enough that we can redirect our subsequent focus to the area of real interest.

nucleus: A double membrane–bound organelle that contains the genetic information of the cell; acts like the brain of the cell; helps control metabolism, movement, and reproduction.

occipital lobe: Rearmost lobe in each cerebral hemisphere of the cerebral cortex of the brain; visual processing center.

parietal lobe: Part of the brain located in upper back of the skull; receives and processes sensory information pertaining to taste, temperature, and touch.

positive punishment: In operant conditioning, adding something noxious to influence behavior. For instance, a teacher might add an unpleasant consequence (detention) to a student's schedule in order to discourage their maladaptive behavior (playing games on his phone during class).

positive reinforcement: In operant conditioning, adding something pleasant that makes the behavior more likely to reoccur. For instance, a teacher might add a pleasant consequence (cookie, star) to a student in order to encourage good behavior.

prefrontal cortex: Part of the brain located at the front of the frontal lobe; implicated in a variety of complex behaviors including higher-order thinking like planning, predicting, and synthesizing; greatly contributes to personality development.

Pygmalion effect: An effect described by Rosenthal and Jacobson (1968) in which teachers were told that certain children would be bloomers (based on IQ scores) and they did indeed show statistically significant gains favoring the experimental group of "intellectual bloomers." This led to the conclusion that teacher expectations, particularly for the youngest children, can influence student achievement.

Reflect: A spoke of the Challenge Wheel where the individual learner interacts with the information presented during the Multiple Perspectives multimedia exposition by referring to three scaffolding questions that guide the process.

REM: Rapid eye movement; jerky motion of a person's eyes occurring in deep sleep while the rest of body is relatively paralyzed (no twisting or turning); REM sleep has benefits for the mind and for the brain as things we learned during the day are processed, consolidating memories we want to keep and getting rid of those that we don't.

Report Out: A spoke of the Challenge Wheel where one member of a collaborative group shares what their small group discovers regarding the challenge as a result of the scaffolded reflection and revised thinking.

reticular activating system (RAS): A portal through which nearly all information enters the brain (exception is smell, which goes directly to the brain's limbic area); a diffuse network of nerve pathways in the brain stem that connects the spinal cord, cerebrum, and cerebellum and mediates the overall level of consciousness.

Revised Thinking: A spoke of the Challenge Wheel where each participant is asked to share the reflection from the previous exercise with a small group; enhances information that was present at Initial Thoughts, after Multiple Perspectives were presented, and as a result of the individual reflection with the aid of the scaffolded questions.

reward–punishment: A method of learning by means of operant conditioning. The behavioral psychologist B. F. Skinner suggested that consequences for behavior (either reward or punishment), would bring about and/or reinforce learning.

routine expert: Mastering procedures in order to become highly efficient and accurate (but not flexible or adaptable in situations that are outside the routine). People who are routine experts can accelerate efficiency through well-practiced routines.

salience: The quality by which something stands out from its neighbors. Saliency detection is considered to be a key attentional mechanism that facilitates learning and survival by enabling organisms to focus their limited perceptual and cognitive resources on the most pertinent subset of the available sensory data.

scaffolding constructs: Meaningful elements that consistently aid the acquisition of Big Ideas through connections to extraneous informational bits.

sensory data: Input from sensory organs (eyes, ears, hands, tongue, skin, nose) that transforms physical stimuli such as touch, heat, sound waves, or photons of light into electrochemical signals.

spatial mapping: A process by which sensory information is relayed to the brain stem for processing into topological map representations.

spiny arbors: Small membranous protrusions from a neuron's dendrite that typically receive input from a single axon at the synapse. Dendritic spines serve as a storage site for synaptic strength and help transmit electrical signals to the neuron's cell body.

synapse: Junction between two nerve cells, consisting of a minute gap across which impulses pass by diffusion of a neurotransmitter; a small gap separating neurons.

temporal lobe: Part of brain associated with auditory processing and olfaction; located in front of the occipital lobe; key to understanding meaningful speech, hearing, and selective listening—attributes vital to learning.

temporary compliance: Use of extrinsic motivators (such as incentives for losing weight or quitting smoking, for example) fail to produce lasting change in attitudes and behavior. For instance, productivity studies demonstrate that rewards and other kinds of incentives are less effective than other strategies, and often prove worse than doing nothing at all.

References

The Beginning Of BcD

1. Ebbinghaus, Hermann. "Memory: A Contribution to Experimental Psychology." *Annals of Neurosciences* 20, no. 4 (2013). https://www.ncbi.nlm.nih.gov/pmc/articles/PMC4117135/

2. Medina, John. *Brain Rules: 12 Principles for Surviving and Thriving at Work, Home, and School.* Seattle, WA: Pear Press. 2008.

3. Miller, George A. "The Cognitive Revolution: A Historical Perspective." *Trends in Cognitive Sciences* 7, no. 3 (2003): 141–144.

Part I: Your Brain: Demystify Three Pounds Of Goop

1.1 Learning Is Connecting The Dots

1. Kaku, Michio. *The Future of the Mind.* Westminster, England: Penguin. 2016.

2. The Endowment for Human Development. "Grasping Large Numbers." https://www.ehd.org/science_technology_largenumbers

3. Logothetis, NK, J. Pauls, T. Trinath, and A. Oeltermann. "Neurophysiological Investigation of the Basis of the FMRI Signal." *PubMed.* July 12, 2001.

4. UC San Diego School of Medicine. "What Is FMRI?" https://fmri.ucsd.edu/Research/whatisfmri.html

1.2 Insulate Your Neurons

1. Costa, L.R.R. "Evaluation & Care of Newborn Foals." American Association of Equine Practitioners. 2016. https://aaep.org/horsehealth/evaluation-care-newborn-foals

1.3 Get To Know Your Sexy Brain Bits

1. Gazzaniga, M.S. "Cerebral Specialization and Interhemispheric Communication: Does the Corpus Callosum Enable the Human Condition?" *Brain* 123, no. 7 (2000): 1293–1326.

2. *The Walking Dead.* Directed by Robert Kerkman, Tony Moore, and Charlie Adlard. New York, NY: AMC Networks Inc. October 31, 2010–present.

3. Kandel, Eric R. and Sarah Mack. *Principles of Neural Science.* New York, NY: McGraw-Hill Medical. 2014.

4. Kimura, Doreen. "Acquisition of A Motor Skill After Left-Hemisphere Damage." *PsycEXTRA Dataset.* 1976. https://academic.oup.com/brain/article-abstract/100/3/527/340172?redirectedFrom=PDF

5. Warrington, E. and L. Weiskrantz. "An Analysis of Short-Term and Long-Term Memory Defects in Man." In J.A. Deutsch, ed. *The Physiological Basis of Memory.* New York: Academic Press. 1973.

6. Benarroch, Eduardo E. *Medical Neurosciences: An Approach to Anatomy, Pathology, and Physiology by Systems and Levels.* Philadelphia: Lippincott Williams & Wilkins. 1999.

7. Dingman, Marc. "Contralateral Neglect." *Neuroscientifically Challenged.* https://neurochallenged.com/glossary/contralateral-neglect

8. Plasticity Brain Centers. "How Your Sense of Taste Works." NeuroSynergy Associates. May 23, 2016. http://www.plasticitybraincenters.com/media/how-your-sense-of-taste-works/

9. Plasticity Brain Centers. "How Your Sense of Smell Works." Neuro-Synergy Associates. June 30, 2016. https://www.plasticitybraincenters. com/media/how-your-sense-of-smell-works/

10. Marek, S. et al. "Spatial and Temporal Organization of the Individual Human Cerebellum." Elsevier (2018): 977–993.

1.4 How Your Brain Filters Information

1. "What Is The Resolution Of The Human Eye In Megapixels?" Forbes.com. October 6, 2016. https://www.forbes.com/sites/ quora/2016/10/06/what-is-the-resolution-of-the-human-eye-in-megapixels/#1002c1885912

2. Mlot, Stephanie. "Quantum Physics Allows for Chicken AND Egg to Come First." *Geek*. Geek.com. September 4, 2018. https://www.geek.com/news/ quantum-physics-allows-for-chicken-and-egg-to-come-first-1751206/

3. Coyle, Daniel. *The Talent Code: Greatness Isn't Born. It's Grown. Here's How.* New York: Bantam Books. 2009.

1.5 Google Is Like Your Hippocampus

1. Scoville, William Beecher and Brenda Milner. "Loss of Recent Memory After Bilateral Hippocampal Lesions." *Journal of Neurology, Neurosurgery, and Psychiatry*. 1957.

1.6 Too Much Information And How To Simplify It

1. Miller, George A. "The Magical Number Seven, Plus or Minus Two: Some Limits on Our Capacity for Processing Information." *Psychological Review* 101, no. 2 (1994): 343–352.

2. Cowan, Nelson. "The Magical Number 4 in Short-term Memory: A Reconsideration of Mental Storage Capacity." *Behavioral and Brain Sciences* 24, no. 1 (2001): 87–114.

3. Maybin, Simon. "Busting the Attention Span Myth." *BBC News*. BBC.com. March 10, 2017. https://www.bbc.com/news/health-38896790

1.7 Prefrontal Cortex: Where We Pay Attention

1. Neubert, Franz-Xaver, Rogier B. Mars, Adam G. Thomas, Jerome Sallet, and Matthew F.S. Rushworth. "Comparison of Human Ventral Frontal Cortex Areas for Cognitive Control and Language with Areas in Monkey Frontal Cortex." *Neuron* 81, no. 3 (2014): 700–713.

2. "Brain Area Unique to Humans Linked to Cognitive Powers." University of Oxford. January 28, 2014. http://www.ox.ac.uk/news/2014-01-28-brain-area-unique-humans-linked-cognitive-powers

3. Mischel, Walter. "Preference for Delayed Reinforcement: An Experimental Study of a Cultural Observation." *The Journal of Abnormal and Social Psychology* 56, no. 1 (1958): 57–61.

4. Mischel, Walter, Ebbe B. Ebbesen, and Antonette Raskoff Zeiss. "Cognitive and Attentional Mechanisms in Delay of Gratification." *Journal of Personality and Social Psychology* 21, no. 2 (1972).

5. Mischel, Walter, Y. Shoda, and M. Rodriguez. "Delay of Gratification in Children." *Science* 244, no. 4907 (1989).

6. Schlam, Tanya R., Nicole L. Wilson, Yuichi Shoda, Walter Mischel, and Ozlem Ayduk. "Preschoolers' Delay of Gratification Predicts Their Body Mass 30 Years Later." *The Journal of Pediatrics* 162, no. 1 (2013): 90–93.

7. Shoda, Yuichi, Walter Mischel, and Philip K. Peake. "Predicting Adolescent Cognitive and Self-Regulatory Competencies from Preschool Delay of Gratification: Identifying Diagnostic Conditions." PDF. *Developmental Psychology* 26 no. 6 (1990): 978–986.

8. Casey, B.J., Leah H. Somerville, Ian H. Gotlib, Ozlem Ayduk, Nicholas T. Franklin, Mary K. Askrend, John Jonides, Marc G. Berman, Nicole L. Wilson, Theresa Teslovich, Gary Glover, Vivian Zayas, Walter Mischel, and Yuichi Shodae. "Behavioral and Neural Correlates of Delay of Gratification 40 Years Later." *Annals of Neurosciences* 19, no. 1 (2012).

1.8 Your World's Gatekeeper

1. MacKinnon, J.B. "The Strange Brain of the World's Greatest Solo Climber." *Nautilus*. August 11, 2016. http://nautil.us/issue/39/sport/the-strange-brain-of-the-worlds-greatest-solo-climber

2. Epel, Elissa S., Elizabeth H. Blackburn, Jue Lin, Firdaus S. Dhabhar, Nancy E. Adler, Jason D. Morrow, and Richard M. Cawthon. "Accelerated Telomere Shortening in Response to Life Stress." *Proceedings of the National Academy of Sciences of the United States of America*. December 7, 2004.

Part II: Learning

2.1 What Is Learning?

2.2 Dopamine: The Intrinsic Shortcut To Learning

1. *Fast Times at Ridgemont High*. Directed by Amy Heckerling. Written by Cameron Crowe. Universal City: Universal Pictures. 1982.

2. Warneken, F. "Altruistic Helping in Human Infants and Young Chimpanzees." *Science* 311, no. 5765 (2006): 1301–1303.

3. Schultz, W., P. Apicella, and T. Ljungberg. "Responses of Monkey Dopamine Neurons to Reward and Conditioned Stimuli During Successive Steps of Learning a Delayed Response Task." *The Journal of Neuroscience* 13 no. 3 (1993): 900–913.

4. Ulber, Julia, Katharina Hamann, and Michael Tomasello. "Extrinsic Rewards Diminish Costly Sharing in 3-Year-Olds." *Child Development* 87, no. 4 (2016): 1192–1203.

2.3 Neuroplasticity: Change Your Brain

1. Hebb, D.O. *The Organization of Behavior: A Neuropsychological Theory.* Mahwah, NJ: L. Erlbaum Ass. 2002.

2. Diamond, Marian Cleeves. *Enriching Heredity: The Impact of the Environment on the Anatomy of the Brain.* New York: Free Press. 1988.

3. McEwen, Bruce S. "Understanding the Potency of Stressful Early Life Experiences on Brain and Body Function." *Metabolism* 57 (2008). https://www.ncbi.nlm.nih.gov/pmc/articles/PMC2567059/

4. Squire, Larry R. "Marian Cleeves Diamond." *The History of Neuroscience in Autobiography.* Volume 6, 2009. 63–96.

5. Suzuki, Wendy. *Healthy Brain, Happy Life: A Personal Program to Activate Your Brain & Do Everything Better.* New York, NY: Harper Collins. 2015.

2.4 Every Thought Counts

1. Disessa, Andrea A. "Why 'Conceptual Ecology' is a Good Idea." *Reconsidering Conceptual Change: Issues in Theory and Practice.* Kluwer Academic Publishers. 2002.

2. Doidge, Norman. *The Brain That Changes Itself: Stories of Personal Triumph from the Frontiers of Brain Science.* London: Penguin Books. 2007.

3. Gundry, Steven R. *The Plant Paradox: The Hidden Dangers in "healthy" Foods That Cause Disease and Weight Gain.* New York, NY: Harper Wave, an Imprint of HarperCollins Publishers. 2017.

4. Coyle, Daniel. *The Talent Code: Greatness Isn't Born. It's Grown. Here's How.* New York: Bantam Books. 2009.

2.5 Pulling It All Together: Neuroscience, Growth Mindset, And You

1. Garland, Eric L., Barbara Fredrickson, Ann M. Kring, David P. John-son, Piper S. Meyer, and David L. Penn. "Upward Spirals of Positive Emotions Counter Downward Spirals of Negativity: Insights from the Broaden-and-build Theory and Affective Neuroscience on the Treatment of Emotion Dysfunctions and Deficits in Psychopathology." *Clinical Psychology Review* 30, no. 7 (2010): 849–864.

2. Rattan, Aneeta, Catherine Good, and Carol S. Dweck. "It's ok—Not everyone can be good at math: Instructors with an Entity Theory Comfort (and Demotivate) Students." *Journal of Experimental Social Psychology* 48, no. 3 (2012): 731–737.

3. "Research on the Use of Khan Academy in Schools." SRI International. SRI.com. https://www.sri.com/work/projects/research-use-khan-academy-schools

4. Rheinberg, Falko, Regina Vollmeyer, and Wolfram Rollett. "Motivation and Action in Self-Regulated Learning." *Handbook of Self-Regulation*, 2000, 503–529.

5. Thorndike, Robert L., Robert Rosenthal, and Lenore Jacobson. "Pygmalion in the Classroom." *American Educational Research Journal* 5, no. 4 (1968): 708.

6. Bezuijen, Xander, Peter van den Berg, and Karen van Dam. "Pygmalion and Employee Learning: The Role of Leader Behavior." *Journal of Management*. 2009.

7. O'Mahony, T.K., C. McQuinn, J. Williamson, N. Abe, H. Buckland, S. Cunningham, editors. "How Do I Learn: National Institutes of Health Study Moves the Needle in Middle School Learning." Barcelona. 2017.

8. "High School/College Brain Breaks." https://brainbreaks-useit.weebly.com/high-schoolcollege-brain-breaks.html

Part III: Behaviorism

3.1 You Get An "A" And You Get An "F"

1. OpenStax College. "Operant Conditioning." LumenLearning.com. Introduction to Psychology. https://courses.lumenlearning.com/wsu-sandbox/chapter/operant-conditioning/

2. Brown, Richard E. "The Life And Work Of Donald Olding Hebb, Canada's Greatest Psychologist." *Proceedings of the Nova Scotian Institute of Science (NSIS)* 44, no. 1 (2007).

3. Hebb, D.O. *The Organization of Behavior: A Neuropsychological Theory.* Mahwah, NJ: L. Erlbaum Ass. 2002.

4. Specter, Michael. "DROOL: Ivan Pavlov's real quest." *The New Yorker.* November 17, 2014. https://www.newyorker.com/magazine/2014/11/24/drool

5. McLeod, Saul. "Pavlov's Dogs." SimplyPsychology.org. 2018. https://www.simplypsychology.org/pavlov.html

3.2 Behaviorism Is Outdated

1. Boyce, W. Thomas. *The Orchid and the Dandelion: Why Some Children Struggle and How All Can Thrive.* Toronto: Penguin Canada. 2019.

2. Miller, Tony. "Partnering for Education Reform." U.S. Department of Education. Ed.gov. July 7, 2011. https://www.ed.gov/news/speeches/partnering-education-reform

3. Banchero, Stephanie. "High-School Graduation Rate Inches Up." *The Wall Street Journal.* WSJ.com. January 22, 2013. https://www.wsj.com/articles/SB10001424127887323301104578256142504828724

4. Craw, Jennifer. "Graduation Rates Worldwide." *National Center On Education and the Economy.* May 30, 2018. http://ncee.org/2018/05/graduation-rates-worldwide/

5. Strauss, Valerie. "Hiding in Plain Sight: The Adult Literacy Crisis." *The Washington Post*. WashingtonPost.com. November 1, 2016. https://www.washingtonpost.com/news/answer-sheet/wp/2016/11/01/hiding-in-plain-sight-the-adult-literacy-crisis/?utm_term=.ec0c5932fd05

6. U.S. Bureau of Labor Statistics. "Employment Trends by Typical Entry-level Education Requirement." *Monthly Labor Review*. September 1, 2017. https://www.bls.gov/opub/mlr/2017/article/employment-trends-by-typical-entry-level-education-requirement.htm.

7. Stephens, R. "The Boeing Company." Testimony before the House Science and Technology Subcommittee on Research and Science Education, Written Testimony. 2010.

8. MacPherson, B. "Changes in the Aeronautical Manufacturing Business." Audio recording. Seattle, WA: LIFE Center, University of Washington. 2006.

3.3 What Your Boss Is Doing Wrong

1. Culatta, Richard. "ADDIE Model." *Instructional Design*. InstructionalDesign.org. https://www.instructionaldesign.org/models/addie/

2. Dick, Walter, Lou Carey, and James O. Carey. *The Systematic Design of Instruction*. Boston: Pearson. 2015.

3. *Ferris Bueller's Day Off*. DVD. Directed by John Hughes. Hollywood, CA: Paramount Pictures. 1986.

4. Stephens R. "Engineering Education from An Industrial Viewpoint." *Complex Adaptive Systems View of Education*. Internal Boeing company paper. 2011.

5. O'Mahony, Timothy K., Nancy J. Vye, John D. Bransford, Elizabeth A. Sanders, Reed Stevens, Richard D. Stephens, Michael C. Richey, Kuen Y. Lin, and Moe K. Soleiman. "A Comparison of Lecture-Based and Challenge-Based Learning in a Workplace Setting: Course Designs,

Patterns of Interactivity, and Learning Outcomes." *Journal of the Learning Sciences* 21, no. 1 (2012): 182–206.

3.4 Why Incentives Don't Work

1. Kohn, Alfie. *Punished by Rewards: The Trouble with Gold Stars, Incentive Plans, As, Praise, and Other Bribes*. Houghton Mifflin Harcourt Trade & Reference Publishers. 2018.

2. Goodman, Brenda. "I Hear Ringing and There's No One There. I Wonder Why." *The New York Times*. NewYorkTimes.com. May 4, 2006. https://www.nytimes.com/2006/05/04/fashion/thursdaystyles/04phan.html

3. "Curve of Forgetting." University of Waterloo. Campus Wellness. https://uwaterloo.ca/campus-wellness/curve-forgetting

4. Ebbinghaus, Hermann. "Memory: A Contribution to Experimental Psychology." *Annals of Neurosciences* 20, no. 4 (2013). https://www.ncbi.nlm.nih.gov/pmc/articles/PMC4117135/

5. Krueger, Gina. "Brain Break Ideas for Teachers." PDF. *MSMSPE*. http://www.msmspe.com/uploads/4/7/1/1/47116129/brain_break_ideas_for_teachers.pdf

Part IV: We All Love A Challenge

4.1 The Educator's Dilemma

1. Nathan, Mitchell J., Kenneth Koedinger, and Martha Alibali. "Expert Blind Spot: When Content Knowledge Eclipses Pedagogical Content Knowledge." Third International Conference on Cognitive Science. Beijing, China: USTC Press. 2001. http://pact.cs.cmu.edu/pubs/2001_NathanEtAl_ICCS_EBS.pdf

4.2 What Rich's Daughter And Jeff Bezos Have In Common

1. Wiggins, Grant and Jay McTighe. *Understanding by Design*. Prentice Hall, Inc. 2000.

2. Savery, John and Thomas Duffy. "Problem Based Learning: An Instructional Model and its Constructivist Framework." Bloomington, IN: Center for Research on Learning Technology. 2001.

3. Dyer, Jeff and Hal Gregersen. "How Does Amazon Stay At Day One?" *Forbes*. Forbes.com. August 8, 2017. https://www.forbes.com/sites/innovatorsdna/2017/08/08/how-does-amazon-stay-at-day-one/#15d65f827e4d

4. Bilton, Nick. "Is Amazon Working Backward?" *The New York Times*. NYTimes.com. December 24, 2009. https://bits.blogs.nytimes.com/2009/12/24/is-amazon-working-backwards/

5. Salter, Chuck. "Kindle 2 Preview: Jeff Bezos on Why Amazon Works Backwards." *Fast Company*. February 6, 2009. https://www.fastcompany.com/90184288/kindle-2-preview-jeff-bezos-on-why-amazon-works-backwards

6. "Billionaires: The Richest People in the World." *Forbes*. Forbes.com. March 5, 2019. Edited by Luisa Kroll and Kerry A. Dolan. https://www.forbes.com/billionaires/#4ab03dd8251c

7. Wiggins, Grant and Jay McTighe. *Understanding by Design*. Prentice Hall, Inc. 2000.

4.3 What's The Big Idea?

1. National Institutes of Health. "The Benefits of Slumber: Why You Need a Good Night's Sleep." *News in Health*. Newsinhealth.nih.gov. April 2013. https://newsinhealth.nih.gov/2013/04/benefits-slumber

4.4 The Big Idea Produces Incredible Results

4.5 Educate Like An Orchestra Conductor

1.   Bereiter, Carl and Marlene Scardamalia. *Surpassing Ourselves: An Inquiry into the Nature and Implications of Expertise.* Chicago: Open Court. 1993.

2.   *Office Space.* DVD. California: 20th Century Fox. 2005.

4.6 The Challenge Wheel

1.   Cook, Clayton R., Aria Fiat, Madeline Larson, Christopher Daikos, Tal Slemrod, Elizabeth Holland, Andrew Thayer, Tyler Renshaw. "Positive Greetings at the Door: Evaluation of a Low-Cost, High-Yield Proactive Classroom Management Strategy." PDF. *Journal of Positive Behavior Interventions.* 20, no. 3 (2018). https://www.continuaconsulting.com/documents/Positive%20Greetings%20at%20the%20Door%20-%20 C.%20Daikos.pdf

2.   O'Mahony, Timothy K., Nancy J. Vye, John D. Bransford, Elizabeth A. Sanders, Reed Stevens, Richard D. Stephens, Michael C. Richey, Kuen Y. Lin, and Moe K. Soleiman. "A Comparison of Lecture-Based and Challenge-Based Learning in a Workplace Setting: Course Designs, Patterns of Interactivity, and Learning Outcomes." *Journal of the Learning Sciences* 21, no. 1 (2012): 182–206.

4.7 Initial Thoughts: Prime The Learning Engine

1.   Bransford, John and Linda Darling-Hammond. *Preparing Teachers for a Changing World: What Teachers Should Learn and Be Able to Do.* California: Jossey-Bass. 2017.

4.8 Multiple Perspectives: Experts Engage The Challenge

1.   "High School/College Brain Breaks." https://brainbreaks-useit.weebly.com/high-schoolcollege-brain-breaks.html

4.9 Reflect: The Art Of Critical Thinking

1. O'Mahony T.K., J. Petz, J. Cook, K. Cheng, and M. Rolandi. "The Design Help Desk: A collaborative approach to design education for scientists and engineers." In Press. 2019.

2. Education Commission of the States. "Equipping Education Leaders, Advancing Ideas." Denver, CO: ECS Report. 2011.

3. Griswold, Alison. "Amazon is hiring fewer workers this holiday season, a sign that robots are replacing them." *Quartz*. QZ.com. November 2, 2018. https://qz.com/1449634/amazons-reduced-holiday-hiring-is-a-bad-sign-for-human-workers/

4. Schlosser, Kurt. "Amazon Now Employs 566,000 People Worldwide—a 66 Percent Jump from a Year Ago." *GeekWire*. GeekWire.com. February 1, 2018. https://www.geekwire.com/2018/amazon-now-employs-566000-people-worldwide-66-percent-jump-year-ago/

4.10 Revised Thinking: Activate Choice And Agency

4.11 Report Out: High-Octane Cognitive Rehearsal

1. De Waal, Frans. *Mama's Last Hug: Animal Emotions and What They Tell Us About Ourselves*. New York: W. W. Norton & Company Inc. 2019.

2. Thompson, Ellen. "Brain-centric Design Transforms a Learning Community Immediately and Forever." The International Conference on E-Learning in the Workplace. Teachers College, New York. 2019.

About Kieran O'Mahony

Dr. Kieran O'Mahony is a founding member of the Institute for Connecting Neuroscience with Teaching and Learning (iCNtl)—a Seattle-based nonprofit that provides professional development for K–12 teachers with a view to improving learning outcomes. As a learning scientist with a focus on cognitive neuroscience, Dr. O'Mahony carried out systems research at the University of Washington College of Education LIFE Center (Learning in Informal and Formal Environments), the first NSF-funded Science of Learning Center that studied the social aspects of how children learn. LIFE consisted of a collaborative research team from several universities and research institutes including the following: University of Washington College of Education, Stanford University College of Education, Stanford Research Institute (SRI), and the Institute for Learning and Brain Science at the University of Washington (ILABS).

As new knowledge is disseminated and insights are made at the biomolecular level in brain labs, and as research results emerge from modern scanning devices, the iCNtl team translates these findings into practices and processes for teaching and learning. The goal is to discover and invent applications that impact teaching and training in schools and workplaces and at home.

Dr. O'Mahony's other research interests include sociocultural perspectives on cognition, learning, graphical representation, and use of technology in formal and informal learning environments. He explores diffusion of innovations systemically across multiple learning environments and stakeholder communities. In particular, he is interested in teacher/learner interaction across various settings, including multidimensional design-based implementation research in various workplace and academic institutions.

Contact: Timothy Kieran O'Mahony, PhD, FRGS

Email: Kieran@icntl.org

About Rich Carr

Optimizing human performance via personal intrinsic agency is at the heart of Rich Carr and his dynamic passions. An INFJ and honored graduate in Mass Media and Mass Communications, Carr is also an army veteran and a decorated graduate of the Department of Defense Information School, Electronic Journalism School, and the renowned Wizard Academy in Austin, Texas.

A Certified Radio Marketing Expert by the Radio Advertising Bureau (CRME, the radio industry's highest sales designation), Carr's skills were honed in his early work for the Country Music Association, which segued into radio station management and eventually radio station ownership throughout Washington state. Clear Channel Communications, Sandusky Broadcasting, Fisher Broadcasting, and Entercom Broadcasting have all sought his sales consulting and the ability to open new markets and set new sales paradigms.

Carr eventually became Director of Digital for Paul Allen's Rose City Radio group, setting sales and innovation records by combining the internet and radio into breathtakingly successful events for advertisers and listeners. On air, Carr was also featured as the host of "The Wired Northwest," a daily look into that region's burgeoning internet-centric rapid growth via technological, digital, and cellular means.

Carr owned and operated radio stations, managed television stations, and started Carr Knowledge in 1999 to ignite audience behavior by focusing on how a message would ease into the brain, be accepted and retained, and enable the learner to act on that new information as their own. Clients such as the Seattle Seahawks, Volkswagen, Nike, Silicon Valley Bank, Aetna, Schnitzer Steel, and a growing cadre of innovative companies are educating their workforces to match the demands of continuous change for the adaptive needs of the enterprise.

Index

Numbers

3Rs
> reading, (w)riting, (a)rithmetic, 200
> Reflect, Revised Thinking, Report Out, 201

1950s, research done in, 187–188

A

acronyms, 40

action potential, 8–10, 201, 215

active avoidance, 96

adaptive expert, 142, 215. *See also* experts

ADD/ADHD, 70

addictive feedback loop, 76

ADDIE (analysis, design, development, implementation, and evaluation), 107

A-F students, 100

agency, 84

aha moments, 101

alcohol, impact of, 24

alertness, 18

"Amy," 51

amygdala. *See also* sensory data
> defined, 215
> as gatekeeper, 51–55
> and PFC (prefrontal cortex), 53

amygdala hijack, 153–154, 215–216

"ancient" brain, 17–18

"animal" brain, 17–18

animals, observing as newborns, 14–15

answers, searching for, 63–64

"Anything, anyone?" syndrome, 108

arousal, focus, and attention, 154

ARPA (Advanced Research Projects Agency), 188

articulating function, 48

assessment, role in Challenge Wheel, 146

attention, arousal, and focus, 45, 47–48, 154, 216

attention span, 45

auditory information, 20

autonomic nervous system, 101

axon communication, 8

axon terminal, 216

axons, 10, 216

B

backward design, 125, 128, 216

balance and executive monitoring, 19, 23–24

behavior
> and frontal lobe, 20
> increasing and decreasing, 96

behaviorism
> versus Brain-centric Design, 132
> versus cognitivists, 108
> establishment of, 189
> fear-based nature of, 113

gatekeeper, amygdala as, 51–55
Gates, Bill, 191
Gerstmann's syndrome, 22
"gifted" label, 77–78
"Good girl!," 103
Google, contrasting to hippocampi, 39–42
GPA, 100
graduation rates, 102
"gray matter," 13
growth mindset, 88, 220
Gundry, Steven, 82

H

happiness, 83
hearing, 18, 20
heart, lungs, and blood pressure, 19–20
Hebb, Donald, 78–79, 94, 198, 220
hemispheres of forebrain, 18
hindbrain, 17–18, 220
Hinton, Geoffrey Everest, 191–193
hippocampus, 39–42, 220
HM, 41–42
homeostasis, 111–113, 220
Honnold, Alex, 53
hyperthymesia, 42

I

IBM, 198
incentives, ineffectiveness of, 111–117
information
    chunking, 133
    passing via neurons, 8
    processing, 30
Initial Thoughts, role in Challenge Wheel, 150, 153–158, 221
intentional practice, 82–83, 221
interpretation, 20
intrinsic motivation, 70–71, 221

"It's all in my head.," 87

J

JASPER (joint attention, symbolic play, engagement, and regulation), 199
job requirements, 105
Joseph, Jane, 53

K

Kaku, Michio, 5
Kindle, 128
knowledge
    activating, 81, 155
    cocreating and activating, 61–63
Kohn, Alfie, 111
KPIs (key performance indicators), 139
Kuhnian paradigm, 195–196

L

learner, role in Challenge Wheel, 146
learning function, 20, 26. *See also* dopamine; teaching
learning scientist, 59–62
lecturing, avoiding, 179
LIFE Center (Learning in Informal and Formal Environments), 199–201
lightning, planning for and managing, 59–60
lobes of brain, 19–22
lungs, heart, and blood pressure, 19–20

M

"The Magical Number Seven," 43, 197
marshmallow test, 49
Me Here Now, 72, 146, 154, 160, 163, 221

Brain-centric Design Coaching, Consulting, And Training Programs

Henry Ford once said, "Whether you believe you can do a thing or not, you are right." Cognitive learning neuroscience has not only verified this but has also given you the model to make it happen for you and your business, and for the fortunate throngs whose potential will be maximized by your energies in implementing Brain-centric Design immediately and indefinitely.

Learning Brain-centric Design ~ www.BraincentricDesign.com

BcD YOURSELF

Experience Brain-centric Design by immersing yourself in each chapter online. More than 30 hours of BcD Challenge Wheel experiences have been developed for you, delivering multiple perspectives and allowing you to interact with the content to make it your thinking. Once you learn BcD, you'll never go back!

BcD YOUR BUSINESS

From the Fortune 500 to the local business, Brain-centric Design and its growing cadre of Brain-centric Instructional Designers (BcID) are ready to transform your company! We'll work with your team to take your existing content out of its current configuration and into one that is brain-centric, saves time, and delivers deep understanding.

BcD YOUR CAREER

Becoming a Brain-centric Instructional Designer (BcID) is the highest certification available in the learning sciences for producing content for deep understanding, and is accredited by the Institute for Connecting Neuroscience with Teaching & Learning. Enabling you to bring critical mental models and methodologies of Brain-centric Design as a Certified BcID gives you the tools and practices that align with how the brain works and how people learn.

It's not clever…it's science.

Made in the USA
San Bernardino, CA
26 June 2019